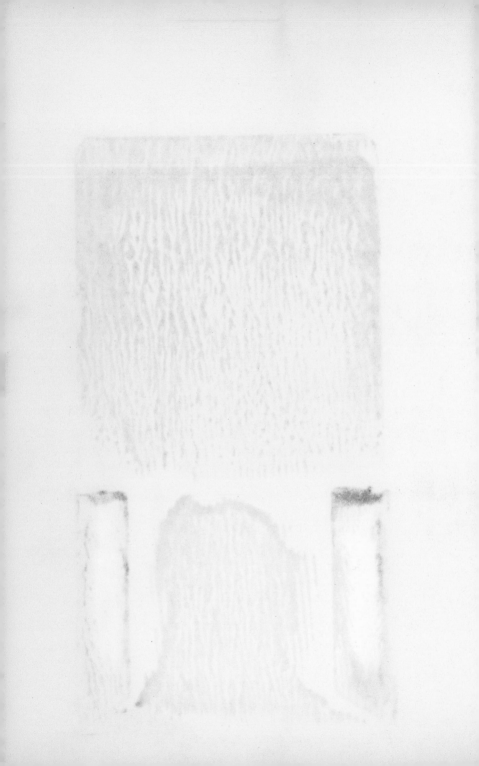

The Oilman's Barrel

The Oilman's Barrel

BY ROBERT E. HARDWICKE

NORMAN : UNIVERSITY OF OKLAHOMA PRESS

By Robert E. Hardwicke

Innocent Purchaser of Oil and Gas Lease (Dallas, 1921)
Petroleum and Natural Gas Bibliography (Austin, 1937)
Antitrust Laws, et al. v. *Unit Operation of Oil or Gas Pools*
(New York, 1948)
The Oilman's Barrel (Norman, 1958)

Library of Congress Catalog Card Number: 58-6857

Copyright 1958 by the University of Oklahoma Press,
Publishing Division of the University.
Composed and printed at Norman, Oklahoma, U.S.A.,
by the University of Oklahoma Press.
First edition.

Introduction

DURING WORLD WAR II, some dozen members of the petroleum industry, who were serving in Washington on the staff of the Petroleum Administration for War, were at lunch. The group was composed of at least one each of the following: operator, transporter, geologist, refiner, marketer, engineer, economist, and lawyer. This question was asked: What was the origin of the 42-gallon barrel that has been adopted or is generally accepted as the unit of measure in the United States for crude oil? No one knew or could offer any rational explanation at the time.

Shortly after the question was asked, several of those who were present at the luncheon did a bit of research, and each suggested a different answer. Such was the beginning of an investigation by me that has continued at short and infrequent intervals over a thirteen-year period. The investigation not only has failed to produce a clearcut answer concerning the 42-gallon oil barrel but has also presented the mystery of the 40-gallon barrel (unit of measure or container) that was used in the oil fields of western Pennsylvania in the early days (1860–70) of the industry.

Frustration is inherent in almost any historical research that involves weights and measures, as I found out about twenty-five years ago when I undertook to establish, in connection with a lawsuit, the meaning of the word "ton" as used in an oil lease in Texas that provided for a royalty of $1.00 a ton on sulphur. The question was whether a short ton of 2,000 pounds or a long ton of 2,240 pounds should be employed in calculating royalty. When the lease was executed, there was no Texas statute that defined a ton; consequently, proof of meaning was necessary. The investigation involved tracing the histories of the changes in the values of the pound and the stone for their bearing on the origin and use of the 100- and 112-pound hundredweights, and study of the consequent use of the 2,000- and 2,240-pound tons, inasmuch as a ton in the English system is 20 hundredweight. Finally, it was necessary to get the facts concerning the meaning, by custom and usage in Texas, of the word "ton," and then to conclude which of several somewhat conflicting principles of law ought to be applied. Fortunately or unfortunately, the case was settled.

That experience should have caused me to let others try to find out why and when the 42-gallon oil barrel was adopted or generally accepted in the United States. Nevertheless, items of interest kept popping up, and my reluctance to investigate was sporadically overcome, with the result that considerable information has been obtained. It is here set down as being of interest and of value should someone else wish to pursue the subject further.

My voluminous file on the oilman's barrel is proof of the tremendous help that has been given by many persons in seeking, furnishing, and checking information. To each of that large group, whose number is too great to mention individually, I offer my thanks.

Robert E. Hardwicke

Fort Worth, Texas
February 10, 1958

Contents

Illustrations

The Oilman's Barrel

How Our Gallon Got That Way

ONE STARTING POINT for finding out the meaning of the term "barrel," and for tracing the variations in its capacity, is the gallon. That is the approach here followed, for the barrel, as a unit of liquid measure or capacity, is defined as containing a stated number of gallons. It seems to be necessary, therefore, to know what a gallon is before we can discuss what a barrel (or a 42-gallon barrel) is.

Edward B. Swanson, who has done considerable research on the origin of the 42-gallon oil barrel, starts at the top, or with the old "tunne" (tonne, tun, or ton), a cask for wine of 252 gallons, and, as will be explained in some detail, he then works down to a 42-gallon barrel by showing how a cask of 42 gallons, which is one-sixth of 252 gallons or one-sixth of a tunne, originated. Even so, what was the size of the gallon and why? And how did it happen that a barrel of 42 gallons of 231 cubic inches, instead of 224 or 269 cubic inches, or some other number of cubic inches to the gallon, was adopted?[1]

[1] Mr. Swanson, who was an economist in the Department

The term "gallon" has been used in England for a long time, and a similar word is found in the Romance languages (F., *gallon;* Sp., *galón;* Pg., *galão;* It., *gallone*). As early as 1266, during the reign of Henry III, a statute provided that "8 pounds do make a gallon of wine, and 8 gallons of wine do make a London bushel, which is the eighth part of a quarter."[2]

In a recent book on metrology, there is a translated quotation from *Tractatus de Ponderibus et Mensuris* as follows:

By consent of the whole realm, the King's measure was made so that an English penny, which is called Sterling, round without clipping, shall weigh thirty-two grains of wheat dry in the midst of the ear; twenty pence make an ounce and twelve ounces

of the Interior in Washington, retired recently, although he spends a good part of his time in collecting historical material for the Petroleum Section of the Library of the Department of the Interior. He was one of the men who was present at the PAW luncheon that is mentioned in the introduction. He, too, became interested in the "barrel," and we have exchanged information ever since. Graciously, he has authorized the use of material developed in his research.

[2] Edward Nicholson, *Men and Measures,* 96. Nicholson uses the date 1267. In *Century Dictionary and Cyclopedia,* under "Gallon," similar information is given, but the date is stated to be 1266, not 1267. The later date appears to be correct. *Pickering's Statutes at Large* (Gt. Brit.), I, 36. Sometimes the confusion concerning dates of statutes in Great Britain occurs from the failure to make clear whether the reference is to the date of the passage of the statute or to the date that it became effective.

make a pound and eight pounds make a gallon of wine and eight gallons of wine make a bushel of London, which is the eighth part of a quarter.[3]

The pound mentioned, the Tower pound, was a lighter one than the troy pound or the avoirdupois pound, which eventually was substituted for the Tower pound. Of interest is the fact that early weights and measures were based on grains of wheat, barley, or "corn" placed in a row to form a unit, as an inch, or on a specified number of the grains to form a unit of weight, as a pound.[4]

[3] A. E. Berriman, *Historical Metrology*, 162. Berriman concludes that the definition of gallon should be interpreted to mean eight pounds of wheat measure. A slightly different translation of the statute that is quoted in the text, but with no change in substance, appears in *Pickering's Statutes at Large* (Gt. Brit.), I, 36, 51 Henry III in 1266. See *Statutes of the Realm*, 117, 25 Edw. I, c. 25 (1297), and also page 204, where the *Tractatus de Ponderibus et Mensuris* appears in the section of statutes of uncertain date. The volumes comprising *Statutes of the Realm* are rare books of extraordinary beauty. Sir Courtenay Ilbert, in the *English Statute Book, Journal of the Society of Comparative Legislation* (new series, 1900), II, 75, says: "[The] edition [was] printed by command of His Majesty's King George III . . . from original records and authentic manuscripts. . . . This edition is nine folio volumes, of which the first was published in 1810, and the last in 1822, and contains the Statutes from Henry III's Provisions of Merton (1235–36) to the last year of the reign of Queen Anne (1713)." The nine volumes (one in two parts) were later supplemented by two index volumes, one in 1824, the other in 1828.

[4] William Hallock and Herbert T. Wade, *Outlines of the Evolution of Weights and Measures and the Metric System*, 8.

It would seem to be evident that a unit based on grains of dry wheat (corn) in the middle of the ear, or on grains of barley (barleycorn or corn) "round and dry," would not be very definite. The encyclopedias state that the word "corn" has been used since ancient times to indicate small particles or grains, as of sand or salt, and in agriculture to mean seeds of cereal plants, including wheat and barley or barleycorn. In England, the words barleycorn and peppercorn are still used. According to a statute of Edward II in 1324, three barleycorns, "round and dry," made an inch,[5] and, indirectly, the length of a barleycorn (one-third of an inch) still survives as a unit of measure in the United States, but only for calculating shoe sizes, "which increase from 4 inches, by barleycorns, in series of 13's."[6]

Returning to the word "corn," its use in the United States refers to "Indian corn" or maize, not to barleycorn or wheat. The point to be made is that whatever grain or seed was used as the basis for a unit of weight or measure, it was not very accurate. It is more than odd that, although the avoirdupois pound has long been defined here and in Great Britain as being 7,000 grains, and the avoirdupois, the troy, and the apothecary weights give the smallest units in grams (27 11/32 or 27 1/3

[5] *Century Dictionary and Cyclopedia*, under "Barleycorn."
[6] *Lincoln Library of Essential Knowledge* (1944 ed.), 1164. According to the book, this is how to find out the length in inches of a number 8 shoe, adult size: 4 plus 13/3 plus 8/3 = 11 inches.

grains avoirdupois equal to 1 dram; 24 grains troy equal 1 pennyweight; 20 grains apothecary equal 1 scruple), recent statutes and weights-and-measures tables do not define or identify "grain," the base unit. It still seems to be a cereal grain, barleycorn or wheat.

J. H. Alexander, in *Universal Dictionary of Weights and Measures,* uses a reverse method for giving the definition of a grain. He says that a pound avoirdupois equals 7,000 grains, and a grain "must be such that 252.458 of these units, in brass, will be in just equilibrium with a cubic inch of distilled water, when the mercury stands at 30 inches in a barometer, and in a thermometer of Fahrenheit at 62 degrees both for the air and for the water."[7] If that is confusing, or if facilities are not available for making the experiment or test, then another approach may be helpful.

The *Century Dictionary and Cyclopedia* defines the "grain" thus:

> The [grain is the] smallest unit of weight in most systems, originally determined by the weight of a plump grain of wheat. In a pound troy or apothecaries' weight there are 5,760 grains, the grain being the 24th part of a pennyweight in the former and the 20th part of a scruple in the latter. The ounce of each therefore contains 480 grains, while in avoirdupois weight, in which the grain is not used, the ounce is equal to 437 1/2 grains and the pound of 7,000 grains."

[7] Page 132.

7

Why it is said that the "grain" is not used in avoirdupois weight is not clear.

A simpler, if not scientific, definition of the grain is: 1/7,000 of a pound avoirdupois, or 1/437.5 of an ounce (av.) or 1/20 of a scruple (apoth.). The trick is to isolate the single "grain" that is the base unit.

Additional confusion and difficulties arise because it is not enough to know that in English metrology so many pounds make a gallon and so many gallons make a barrel, for there have been several pounds and several gallons. An accurate calculation or understanding of the meaning of the terms "pound," "gallon," and "barrel" requires selection of the right pound, the right gallon, and the right barrel, at the right time.

From 1266, the date of the statute of Henry III, to the reign of Queen Anne (1702–14), significant changes occurred in the use and values of the three pounds: the Tower pound, the troy pound, and the avoirdupois pound. The Saxon pound is thought to be the earliest in the English system. It came to be known as the Tower pound, the old mint pound that was kept in the Tower of London. It weighed 5,400 grains, and was coined in 240 pence or 20 shillings. The troy pound, a French migrant, was in use as early as 1415 and became legal for gold and silver by 1527. The Tower pound was abolished by Henry VIII in favor of a substitute pound of 5,760 grains, the figure at which the troy and apothecaries pound still remain. The old merchant pound, in use with troy, weighed 6,720 grains; it was established about 1270 for all commodities except gold, silver, and medicines, but was superseded about 1330 by the avoirdupois pound, which became the standard at 7,000 grains.[8]

Substantial variations also occurred in the number of cubic inches in a gallon.[9] A good part of the account that will be given in the next few pages concerning the English wine gallon prior to 1700 is based on a letter from Edward B. Swanson, and, with only a few changes, his language has been used.[10]

Bordeaux, the capital of the province of Gironde in southwestern France and the source of the Gascoigne wine referred to in the Statute of 1423, was occupied by the British and was under British dominion from 1154 to 1453. This was the field upon which was fought the Hundred Years' War between England and France, and it was here, with the aid of Joan of Arc, that the English troops finally were forced from the Duchy of Gas-

[8] *Encyclopaedia Britannica* (1949 and 1957 editions) under "Pound"; Nicholson, *Men and Measures,* 147. By a proclamation of December 16, 1587, the long-used avoirdupois pound was established, and the use of the troy pound was prohibited except for gold, silver, and electuaries; Berriman, *Historical Metrology,* 147.

[9] In *Century Dictionary and Cyclopedia,* under "Gallon," a short account is given of the changes in capacity. A more elaborate account was given by F. G. Skinner in the article, "The Imperial Gallon and Its Forerunners from Saxon to Modern Times," published in London in *The Monthly Review of the Institute of Weights and Measures Administration* (May, 1953), 116ff.

[10] November 4, 1955.

9

coigne. There was substantial trade between the two countries during the three centuries, especially in corn, fish, and wine. British authority prevailed in the land whence the wine came; hence, the British prescribed the types and capacities of the casks used in the trade.

The ton was established as the unit of measurement for cargoes and for determining the cargo-carrying capacity of the vessels. It measured forty cubic feet for dry cargo, and thirty-two cubic feet for wine. Corn, being of less specific gravity than wine, in the rough proportion of five to four, would require larger space in the same proportion for the packing of a ton. The *International Encyclopedia* states that the "ton" or "tun" was established as the equivalent of forty cubic feet, and still is so considered in freighting ships unless the bulk exceed 2,240 pounds (or 2,000 pounds in the United States), in which event the charge is made by weight.

The ton weighed 2,016 old English pounds and consisted of 252 gallons of 216 cubic inches each (a wine gallon weighed eight pounds, according to the old English law of Henry III).

Next, the cubic content of the gallon can be calculated. The Tower penny weighed 22 1/2 grains troy. This was the weight of the 32 kernels of corn (wheat) from the middle of the ear. Twenty pennies made an ounce, and there were 15 ounces in the pound by which corn and wine then were weighed commercially. Multiplication of 22 1/2 × 20 × 15 gives 6,750 as the number of grains in a pound, and, as we have seen, eight pounds made a gallon of wine, so a gallon of wine weighed 54,000 grains. A cubic inch of Bordeaux wine weighed 250 grains, so the cubical content of the gallon is determined by dividing 54,000 by 250, which gives 216 cubic inches.

The next calculation is to find the number of fifteen-ounce pounds in a ton, which has been stated as being 2,016 old English pounds. There were 252 gallons at 216 cubic inches per gallon in a ton, or a total of 54,432 cubic inches per ton. A cubic inch of Bordeaux wine is equal to 250 grains troy. Multiplication gives the grains troy in a ton as 13,608,000 (216 × 252 × 250). Since there were 6,750 grains troy in a fifteen-ounce pound, by dividing 13,608,000 by 6,750, the result is 2,016, being the number of pounds in a ton.

Actually, the specific gravity of water was taken in these calculations as being the same as that of wine. The wine referred to is that of Gascoigne, the sort of wine that now goes under the classification of claret or Bordeaux. Its specific gravity is lighter than that of water (9,935 to 10,000). Recognition of this difference in specific gravity accounts for the difference between the early English wine gallon and the standard Irish gallon of 217.6 cubic inches.

The wine gallon of 216 cubic inches (Statute of 1266) was an exact one-eighth of the English cubic foot, or 1,728 cubic inches. It was, therefore, the "congius" of the Romans, weighing ten nummulary and eight commercial pounds and measuring exactly the eighth part of a cubic foot. "Congius" also is the pharmaceutical name for gallon, being represented on prescriptions—should a quantity of that magnitude be prescribed—by the abbreviation "Cong."

A wine gallon of 231 cubic inches had a substantial background even before the 1707 enactment of Queen Anne. It was so made by the rule of *Compositio Mensurarum,* the statute of 1304. It was based also on the Guildhall gallon of 224 cubic inches established by the act of 1496. This was a period of errors and misunderstanding. Although kept in the exchequer, the standard measures established earlier had fallen into decay, and renovation was required. In 1494, after the termination of the long war between the houses of York and Lancaster, Henry VII, then in the tenth year of his reign, undertook to furnish forty-three of the principal cities of the kingdom with new copies of all the standard weights and measures then in the exchequer. They were made and distributed, but it was soon found that all were defective. The statute of 1496 (sometimes cited as 1497) was an attempt to remedy the errors, but it, too, was founded on mistakes. It produced the Guildhall gallon of 224 cubic inches; however, that was based on the use of the pennyweight troy, rather than the penny of the old Tower pound. Swanson adds that the 32 kernels of corn (wheat) under the troy weight would occupy 1/32nd less space than under the old Tower pound, accounting for the difference between the gallon of 224 cubic inches and that of 231 cubic inches.

According to the *Century Dictionary and Cyclopedia,*

"The wine-gallon universally used in the latter part of the Seventeenth Century contained 224.4 cubic inches, while 8 avoirdupois pounds of British wine (of gooseberry or elderberry) measure about 226 inches." The old statutes provided that eight pounds of wine made a gallon, but they failed to say what kind of wine, so, of course, the standard was insufficient.

The need for a statute and an accurate standard to clear up confusion concerning the wine gallon was evident before 1700. The following account draws heavily on the story of the English gallon as told by F. G. Skinner.[11] The Winchester gallon of Henry VII was a vessel that contained 100 troy ounces of wheat as threshed and leveled off brimful. The vessel was checked by the Standards Department of the British Board of Trade in 1931, and was found to contain 268.43 cubic inches. Elizabeth adopted the Winchester gallon of Henry VII and had a bronze gallon prepared that also was checked in 1931 and was found to contain 268.97 cubic inches. The use of wheat to determine weight or capacity did not produce great accuracy, as the size and weight of grains varied with the quality and atmospheric conditions. This led to the passage of a statute in the reign of William III (1702) that gave this definition of the Winchester bushel: "A plain cylindrical vessel, with flat, even bottom, 18 1/2 inches internal diameter by 8 inches deep inside, and having a capacity of 2,150.42 cubic inches." Since a gallon in the English system was one-eighth of

[11] Skinner, *loc. cit.*, 116.

a bushel, one-eighth of William's Winchester bushel gave a gallon of 268.8 cubic inches, being quite close to the Winchester gallons of Henry VII and Elizabeth.

The standard placed in the Guildhall in 1688 was a gallon of 224 (224.2) cubic inches, yet an act in 1689 seemed to provide for a gallon of 231 cubic inches. A lawsuit was the prime factor leading to Parliamentary action to clear up the confusion. The case involved the tax applicable to the importation of "butts" of wine, a "butt" being defined as early as 1484, during the reign of Richard III, as containing 126 gallons.

Skinner tells the story as follows:

This 224 cubic inch standard, though used at the Guild Hall, had no statute of Parliamentary authority behind it as was discovered in a legal dispute in A.D. 1700, involving Excise duties on imported wine, from Alicant in Spain. The defendant, a wine merchant named Thomas Barker, having imported 60 "butts" (of 126 gallons each) had paid duty on them as 60 butts. The Customs Officers declared that by their gauging, each butt contained more than 126 gallons, by their gallon measure which contained 231 cubic inches. Barker contended that the correct gallon was the Elizabeth Winchester gallon (269 cubic inches) kept in the Treasury and that this was the only gallon for which there was statutory authority and in this he was supported by a great number of merchants, vintners and masters of ships, who gave evidence that Spanish wines had always been imported by that measure.

Searches revealed there was no statutory authority for either the Guild Hall wine gallon of 224 cubic inches or for the Customs officers' wine gallon of 231 cubic inches and the Crown case against the defendant collapsed. To save continuing loss of Excise revenue, and because the Court of Exchequer was unable to solve the problem, the Attorney General decided to apply to Parliament to have a standard wine gallon made for the Treasury, to agree with Customs and Excise measure of 231 cubic inches.[12]

The evidence before the Parliamentary committee was sufficient to establish long continued use of a gallon of 231 cubic inches; consequently, in 1706 (effective 1707), by a statute of Queen Anne, that volume was confirmed and a standard established as follows:

Any round vessel (commonly called a cylinder) having an even bottom, and being seven inches diameter throughout, and six inches deep from the top of the inside to the bottom, or any vessel containing two hundred thirty-one cubical inches, and no more, shall be deemed and taken to be a lawful wine gallon.

The 231-cubic-inch gallon was and is generally known as the wine gallon or Queen Anne's gallon. The same

[12] *Ibid.*, 118.

statute provided that 252 gallons of 231 cubic inches of wine made a "ton," 126 gallons made a "butt" or "pipe," and 63 gallons made a "hogshead."[13]

According to Edward Nicholson, the adoption of the wine gallon of 231 cubic inches was in part influenced by these factors: the desire to have a measure that would hold 8 pounds of wine (about 222 cubic inches); the character of wine measures used at ports; the relation to the corn gallon (8 pounds of wheat, not corn); and the fact that 231 cubic inches was the capacity of a cylinder 7 inches in diameter inside and 6 inches deep.[14]

The Queen Anne wine gallon remained the gallon in use in Great Britain until the act of 1824, which adopted the Imperial gallon as a unit of capacity or liquid measure, being 10 pounds of water at 62° Fahrenheit. Such a gallon was by the statute declared to be 277.274 cubic inches. The act of 1824 was repealed by the Weights and Measures Act of 1878. That act made no change in the definition of a gallon (10 pounds of water at 62° Fahrenheit), but there was no declaration of the number of cubic inches in a gallon. After the passage of the

[13] A statute of 1706, designated as 5 Anne c. 27, Sec. 17, effective May 1, 1707, provided that there should be only one legal gallon. *Pickering's Statutes at Large* (Gt. Brit.), XI, 265; also in *Statutes of the Realm,* VIII, 613, 618. The statute established the standard for the gallon in the language quoted in the text, but it did not become effective until 1707; consequently, that date is usually given as the date of the statute.

[14] Nicholson, *Men and Measures,* 114.

act of 1878, a more accurate determination of the weight of water in a cubic foot and a cubic inch was made, and, as a result, the Standards Department of the British Board of Trade for many years has accepted 277.42 cubic inches as the correct capacity in inches of the Imperial gallon.[15]

The British colonists in America brought with them the English system of weights and measures; consequently, the Queen Anne wine gallon of 231 cubic inches was, by usage and by several state statutes, a fairly well established unit for liquid measure in the United States when the Imperial gallon of 277.274 or 277.42 cubic inches was adopted in Great Britain in 1824, displacing the Queen Anne gallon that had been used for a long time.

The experiences of our colonial forefathers with the lack of uniformity in weights and measures throughout the colonies, the variations in the standards that were available, and the shortage of standards that purported to be accurate led to the inclusion in the Constitution of the United States of Article I, Section 8, paragraph 5, that gives to the Congress the power to "fix the Standard of Weights and Measures."

It is indeed odd that the Congress has not yet passed a comprehensive statute on the subject even directly

[15] Berriman, *Historical Metrology*, 175; *Measurement of Oil in Bulk: Standard Weights and Measures*, 26–27 (a booklet published in 1932 in London by the Institution of Petroleum Technologists); Skinner, *loc. cit.*, 116.

17

defining a gallon. The nearest approach is considered to be the act of July 28, 1866, still in force, which authorized the use of the metric system and gave equivalents in what may be called United States units; but the act is permissive, not mandatory.[16]

In the absence of comprehensive federal legislation fixing weights and measures, the states have been free to legislate and have done so; but, as might have been anticipated, uniformity is lacking for many units of measure, especially the barrel. As of January 1, 1950, every state, as well as Alaska, the District of Columbia, Hawaii, Porto Rico, and the Virgin Islands, had passed weights and measures statutes, and most of them could be classed as comprehensive.[17]

The statutes of Arizona, California, Connecticut, the District of Columbia, Florida, Kansas, Maryland, Minnesota, Missouri, Nebraska, New Hampshire, New Jersey, North Carolina, Pennsylvania, South Dakota, and Wisconsin, as of 1950, provide that the unit of liquid capacity is the gallon of 231 cubic inches. The statutes of some

[16] 14 Stat. 339, 15 United States Code (U.S.C.), Section 204.

[17] The federal government published in 1951, in a book of 1,182 pages, a compilation of statutes entitled *Federal and State Weights and Measures Laws Through 1949 Enactments,* being *Circular 501* of the National Bureau of Standards. Examination of the statutes shows the variations. For instance, in Alabama (p. 46) and North Carolina (p. 721), the barrel for liquids is 42 gallons, while in Texas (p. 976), it is 31 1/2 gallons, as it is in most states. There are variations in barrels for different commodities, such as for apples, limes, cranberries, beer, and flour, as the compilation will show.

states and territories provide that the standards adopted by the United States shall be the standards for those states or territories. The gallon is not defined in some states. Of more interest is the fact that no statute has been found that defines a barrel for crude oil or for oil (petroleum) for all purposes. In Alabama and North Carolina the barrel for liquids is 42 gallons, and in Connecticut each vehicle or container of preheated petroleum products must be accompanied by a delivery ticket showing data such as weight and quantity expressed in gallons or in barrels of 42 gallons per barrel. In Louisiana a severance tax on crude oil is calculated on each "barrel of 42 gallons."[18]

In the early days of the Union, President George Washington vigorously urged comprehensive legislation on weights and measures, as did Thomas Jefferson and John Quincy Adams, each while serving as secretary of state.[19] In response to a resolution of the House of Representatives, Jefferson made a report, dated July 4, 1790 (often referred to as the Report of 1793),[20] in which he expressed the belief that some of the long-used English units and terms should be retained, but he urged defi-

[18] *State of Louisiana* v. *Standard Oil Co. of La.*, 188 La. 978, 178 So. 601 (1937).

[19] Hallock and Wade, *Outlines of the Evolution of Weights and Measures and the Metric System.* Chapter IV contains a short history of efforts to obtain a comprehensive federal statute.

[20] 1 Cong., 2 sess., *House Doc. No. 15;* also found in *American State Papers,* Class X, Misc. Vol. I, 13–20; *Works of Jefferson,* VII, 472–95.

nitions that would result in accuracy. He observed that a committee appointed in 1757 by the British House of Commons reported substantial variations in the "gallon" in English metrology, causing ambiguity and confusion. Fourteen different gallons were listed, ranging from 224 cubic inches to 282 cubic inches. Jefferson recommended the adoption of a 270-cubic-inch gallon.

He also submitted an ingenious system devised by him. It was a decimal system, partly because Jefferson had already seen the merits of a decimal system for money that the Congress had adopted and had read discussions of the metric system that had been invented and would be proposed for adoption in France.

In Jefferson's weights-and-measures proposal, the fundamental unit of length was the "foot," derived by "taking one-fifth of the length of the rod forming the second's pendulum and then employing multiples and sub-multiples in building up a series of measures of length." The Jefferson foot differed slightly from the twelve-inch foot in common use. The squares and cubes formed units for area and volume.[21] Clearly, the Jefferson plan was an ex-

[21] A table showing names and units in the Jefferson system is as follows:

10 points make one line
10 lines make one inch
10 inches make one foot
10 feet make one decad
10 decads make one rood
10 roods make one furlong
10 furlongs make one mile

**Samuel M. Kier, the first large-scale marketer
of petroleum in America.**

From the collection of Ernest C. Miller

**A "banknote" used by Kier in advertising
his petroleum "medicine."**

cellent one, but, in spite of a favorable committee report in 1792, Congress did not legislate on the subject.

Although the need for comprehensive federal legislation was recognized as being great, it is likely that the adoption by the French of the metric system in 1795 was the prime stimulus for the resolutions by the houses of Congress (the Senate in 1817 and the House in 1819) calling upon John Quincy Adams, then secretary of state, to investigate the various systems and to make a report, together with his recommendations. The report, made in 1821, was entitled "Report upon Weights and Measures."[22] It is a classic in metrology, not only in subject matter, but also in style.[23]

Adams carefully compared the English and the metric systems, and, while expressing great admiration for the metric, he concluded that it would be impractical to abandon the English system that had been in use for so

Hallock and Wade discuss at some length the Jefferson system and deplore the failure of the Congress to adopt it. It is observed that Jefferson's decimal system was formally offered in 1790. The metric system in France became legal by a law of April 7, 1795. Berriman, *Historical Metrology*, 143.

[22] 16 Cong., 2 sess., *House Doc. No. 109*. See also 16 Cong., 2 sess., *Senate Doc. No. 119*.

[23] William H. Seward, *Life and Public Services of John Quincy Adams*, 236, quotes an eminent Englishman as writing: "The author has thrown more light into the history of our Old English Weights and Measures than all former writers on the same subject." Hallock and Wade, *Outlines of the Evolution of Weights and Measures and the Metric System*, 115–16, were equally complimentary.

long a time. He did recommend the passage of a weights-and-measure statute in which the units would be clearly defined, thus obtaining uniformity throughout the country; however, the Congress of the period failed to follow the recommendation, as it had failed to follow similar ones by Washington and by Jefferson, and, as already observed, no subsequent Congress has legislated comprehensively on weights and measures.

The report by Adams contained a digest of the state statutes, to show some of the variations existing at the time. It appeared, for instance, that in Massachusetts (act of 1692) a "tierce" contained 42 gallons and a barrel 31 1/2 gallons; in New York (act of 1703), a "tight" barrel of 31 1/2 gallons was a wine measure; in New Jersey (act of 1774), a barrel was defined as 31 1/2 wine gallons; in Pennsylvania (act of about 1700), a "tierce" was 42 gallons and a barrel 31 1/2; in Maryland (act of 1745), the statute declared that barrels of flour and bread should be of a size to contain 31 1/2 wine gallons, while a statute passed in 1818, relating to fish barrels or casks, declared that the "tierce" should contain not less than 45 gallons; a Virginia act of 1631–32 provided for a barrel of corn of 5 bushels, Winchester measure, 40 gallons to the barrel, while an act of 1795 provided for a fish barrel of 30 to 32 gallons, and a later act declared that a barrel of salt should contain 5 bushels, the equal of 40 wine gallons.

The statutes digested by Adams showed that in several of the states the gallon or wine gallon was 231 cubic inches, while the beer or ale gallon was 282 cubic inches.

It should now be clear, and could be made clearer, why it was said that frustration is inherent in research that involves the origin, use, and definition of many units or terms applicable to weights and measures.

Although the Congress of the United States has not yet passed a comprehensive weights-and-measures statute, it has directly defined or authorized the definition of some units, and has provided for the establishment of a number of accurate standards.[24] A committee of the Senate, in 1829 or 1830—some nine years after the Adams' report was made—informed the Senate that there were many differences in the standards then in use at custom-houses. This prompted the adoption of a resolution on May 29, 1830, as follows:

Resolved, That the Secretary of the Treasury be directed to cause a comparison to be made of the standards of weights and measures now used at the principal custom-houses in the United States, and report to the Senate at the next session of Congress.

The Secretary of the Treasury submitted to the Senate the reports of March 3, 1831, and June 20, 1832, made to the Secretary by Ferdinand R. Hassler, at that time superintendent of the Coast Survey. The Hassler reports confirmed the existence of large discrepancies in stand-

[24] *Federal and State Weights and Measures Laws Through 1949 Enactments,* 7–40.

ards; consequently, the Secretary of the Treasury, who gave broad interpretation to the 1830 resolution, proceeded without further authority to fix or define several units and to prepare standards. In transmitting the reports to the Senate, the Secretary, Louis McLane, said that the liquid measure would be the wine gallon of 231 cubic inches. These basic units were selected for definition and for preparing standards: a yard of 36 inches, an avoirdupois pound of 7,000 grains, a gallon of 231 cubic inches, and a bushel of 2,150.42 cubic inches. They were all in common use in the 1830's. Standards were carefully prepared under direction of the Treasury, but it was not until the joint resolution of the Congress of June 14, 1836, that the Secretary was instructed to distribute those standards to the customhouses and to the governor of each state.[25]

This is not the place to give details regarding the dis-

[25] *Ibid.*, 1–3. See 15 United States Code (U.S.C.) Section 201, for a provision in the act of March 3, 1881, 21 Stat. 521, directing the secretary of commerce to deliver a set of standards to the governor of each state that had received a grant of land for an agricultural college. Considerable historical information is given in the Hassler Report, also in the report by Louis A. Fischer entitled *Modern Weights and Measures.* The Fischer Report has been published several times by the Bureau of Standards.

A carefully documented and interesting account of the steps taken by the Continental Congress to secure uniformity in weights and measures in the years from 1775 to 1838 may be found in Sarah Ann Jones, "Weights and Measures in Congress," an M.A. thesis at George Washington University, published in booklet form by the Government Printing Office.

tribution of standards, including the one for the gallon, to the governors of the states. However, there does appear to be justification for quoting from a letter of October 28, 1957, from Lewis V. Judson, of the National Bureau of Standards:

As to the standards sent to the Governors of the States it appears that all States except Oklahoma were sent sets of standards. Several of the States have claimed that their standards were never received. In a number of instances the standards were destroyed by fire and in other instances the standards were simply listed as lost. Sometimes the sets of standards were replaced by the Federal government; in other cases individual replacement standards were sent; in some others nothing has been done.

Briefly the distribution of standards was described by L. A. Fischer in NBS Miscellaneous Publication No. 64, "History of the Standard Weights and Measures of the United States" (now out of print) as follows: "By 1838 the weights for the States were reported finished, and during the following year the weights for the customhouses were completed and delivered. By 1850 practically all the States admitted to the Union had been supplied with complete sets of weights and measures, and in addition sets were presented to England, France, Japan, and Siam. As new States were admitted they were also supplied with sets of standards, the last set being supplied to North Dakota in 1893." Apparently the set for North Dakota was the last one issued.

Probably you are especially interested in Texas. This is an example of a State in which the issuance of the standards was somewhat complicated. A set of weights and measures was delivered previous to 1847 and subsequently returned. Another set was delivered in 1858. In November 1879 there is a note that the quart measure bearing serial number 86 was delivered to Texas, but there is a later note stating that it probably was not sent. On November 9, 1881, the 1858 set of standards was destroyed by fire. It was replaced in 1882.

In many cases the State standards furnished by the Federal government have been replaced by more modern standards purchased by the States. These replacement standards have been submitted to the National Bureau of Standards for calibration and certification.

The above statements do not cover that portion of your request in which you ask for the date that each State received its standards. As you will see from the information given about Texas, one cannot, in general, give a single date for the receipt of the standards in a State. Because of the involved nature of the problem, it is not practical to supply the detailed information at this time.

Metric standards were distributed to the States as directed in a joint resolution of Congress dated July 27, 1866.

Although a standard for a gallon of 231 cubic inches was prepared and approved by the Congress, at least indirectly, no federal statute has been found that defines the gallon generally as a vessel containing 231 cubic inches or that defines the gallon as a unit of liquid measure, such as was done in Great Britain for the Imperial gallon.

In the absence of a federal statute defining a "gallon," it is thought to be odd that only a few reported decisions by the courts have been found in which the meaning of the term "gallon" was an issue. In each, the court held that in the United States the "gallon" is a measure of 231 cubic inches.[26]

In *Nichols* v. *Beard,* the question was whether the import tax on ale and stout should be calculated on the wine gallon of 231 cubic inches or the beer barrel of 282 cubic inches. The court held that the gallon of 231 cubic inches was applicable. The opinion of the court traces the history of the use of the wine gallon in the United States; it refers to the resolution of the Congress of June 14, 1836, and the adoption by the secretary of the treasury of a gallon of 231 cubic inches, followed by preparation of standards and their distribution to customhouses and to the states; it also gives definitions from dictionaries and from *Appleton's Cyclopedia* in support of the

[26] *Nichols* v. *Beard,* 15 Fed. 435 (C.C.D. Mass. 1883); *Ceballos* v. *United States,* 146 Fed. 380 (C.C.A. 2d Cir. 1906, affirming 139 Fed. 705); *State of Louisiana* v. *Standard Oil Co. of La.,* 188 La. 978, 178 So. 601 (1937).

holding that the tax statute contemplated a gallon of 231 cubic inches, since no different definition was given in the tax statute under consideration.

The case of *Ceballos* v. *United States* involved the importation of olives—whether the tax of fifteen cents a gallon should be calculated on a gallon of 231 cubic inches or one of 268.8 cubic inches. The importer argued that the gallon of 231 cubic inches was a liquid measure and therefore the dry-measure gallon of 268.8 cubic inches should be used for olives. The opinion of the court does not show why the gallon of 268.8 cubic inches was thought to be applicable; however, it appears that it is one-eighth of 2,150.42 cubic inches, the bushel as fixed under the authority of the resolution of May 29, 1830, and the joint resolution of the houses of Congress dated June 14, 1836. As already pointed out, one-eighth of the bushel of William III measured 268.8 cubic inches, almost the same as the Winchester gallons of Henry VII and Elizabeth. The court, in an informative opinion, held that the gallon of 231 cubic inches should be used in calculation of the tax, as that was the established gallon, and it should be used for olives and other commodities, liquid or dry, since the tax statute had not provided otherwise.

The most recent reported case that has been found in which the meaning of "gallon" was at issue is *State of Louisiana* v. *Standard Oil Company of Louisiana*, decided in 1937. There a severance tax was imposed upon oil produced, to be computed on each "barrel of 42 gallons." The Louisiana court, after giving a short history of the gallon in the United States, held that the 231-cubic-inch gallon was well established and that this measure was applicable in the severance tax. It appears that the Louisiana Legislature, as of January 1, 1950, as shown in the compilation called *Federal and State Weights and Measures Laws,* had not specifically defined "gallon," although in 1948 an act was passed that adopted the standards received under the joint resolutions of the Congress of June 14, 1836, and July 27, 1866, or "such weights and measures in conformity therewith as shall be supplied by the State . . . when . . . certified by the National Bureau of Standards."

Thus it was that by indirection in the 1830's, and by custom, usage, state statutes, and court decisions, the gallon in the United States became and is the same as the wine gallon or Queen Anne's gallon of 231 cubic inches, unless a different definition is given, as in a statute or contract. Frequently, the reference is to the "U. S. gallon," meaning a gallon of 231 cubic inches.

The Barrel Through the Years

HAVING TRACED the history of the gallon, the discussion now turns to the barrel. There is evidence of the use in England, Scotland, and Ireland of the word "barrel" for many centuries, although its meaning varied from time to time, as affected by statute, custom, and the commodity for which the container was to be used.

The word "barrel," according to the *Century Dictionary and Cyclopedia,* is an ancient one of uncertain origin, perhaps of Celtic derivation. There is a similar term with a similar meaning in several languages. The following quotation (the dates in the brackets have been added) is from the *Century Dictionary and Cyclopedia* under Barrel:

As a measure of capacity, the quantity of anything, liquid or solid, which a barrel should contain. In English metrology there were four principal kinds of barrels: the wine-barrel of 31 1/2 gallons; the London ale barrel of 32 beer gallons; the country ale-and beer-barrel of 34 beer gallons; and the London beer-barrel of 36 beer gallons. The wine-barrel was legalized in the reign of Richard III [1483–85], the others under Henry VIII [1509–47]. Under George III [1760–1820] the barrel of ale or beer for town and country was made 36 gallons. Oil, spirits, tar, and pork were measured by the wine-gallon; vinegar, by the barrel of 34 gallons. A barrel of eels or herrings contained 30 gallons by a statute of Henry VI [1422–61], but by another of Edward IV [1461–83] this was made 42 gallons. Salmon and spruce beer were also measured by barrels of 42 gallons. A barrel of beef, wet codfish, or honey contained 32 wine gallons; but honey was sometimes

sold by barrels of 42 gallons of 12 pounds each. By
a statute of George III [1760–1820], a barrel of fish
was made 38 wine gallons; but a barrel of salt pilch-
ards or mackerel measured 50 gallons. . . . There
were besides a great variety of other barrels in Scotland and Ireland.

During the reign of Edward IV (1461–83), considerable skulduggery was prevalent in packing fish in containers, causing the passage of a statute in 1482 that reads
in part as follows (spelling modernized):

Whereas divers Deceits have been used and done,
as well in the Measures of Vessels called Butts, Barrels, and half Barrels ordained for Salmon, and Barrels, half Barrels, and Firkins ordained for Herrings,
Eels, and other barrelled Fish, as in the packing in
the same Vessels of every of the said Fishes before
named, to the great Damage of the King, the Lords
Spiritual and Temporal, and other of the King's
faithful Subjects: For Reformation whereof, our said
Sovereign Lord the King, by the Advice, Assent, and
Authority aforesaid, hath ordained and enacted,
That no Merchant Stranger nor Denizen, after the
Feast of St. Michael next coming, shall sell nor set
to Sale any Salmon by Butt, Barrel, or half Barrel,
or any other vessel, before it be seen, except the
same Butt do hold and contain Fourscore and four
Gallons, the Barrel Two and forty gallons, the half
Barrel One and twenty gallons, well and truly
packed, upon Pain of forfeiture for every Butt, Bar-

rel and half Barrel so failing their said Measure, Six Shillings and Eight Pence.[1]

The barrel, as well as other terms and units, were precisely defined in the reign of Richard III (1483–84) as follows:

Every ton of wine should contain 252 gallons.

Every butt of wine should contain 126 gallons.

Every pipe of wine should contain 126 gallons.

Every tarcian or puncheon should contain 84 gallons.

Every hogshead should contain 63 gallons.

Every tierce should contain 42 gallons.

Every barrel should contain 31 1/2 gallons.

Every rondlet should contain 18 1/2 gallons.

The fish barrel of 42 gallons, provided for by the statute of 1482, was not defined, but it does not follow that the statute of Edward IV was repealed.

The above units, as defined in the reign of Richard III, were confirmed twice in the reign of Henry VIII (1509–47).[2] Some of the terms and units are still in use; others are obsolete, at least in the United States.

[1] 22 Edw. IV c. 11 (1482).

[2] 1 Richard III c. 13 in *Statutes of the Realm*, II, 497; confirmed by 23 Henry VIII c. 7, Sec. 8, and 28 Henry VIII c. 14, Sec. 5 in *Statutes of the Realm*, III, 375, 670.

Raphael Holinshed, in his monumental *Chronicles of England, Scotlande, and Irelande,* published in London in 1577, gave interesting information about weights and measures of the time. He first told about weights in the Third Book, chapter 23, then about liquid measures.[3] With respect to the latter, this appears in chapter 24, Third Book, beginning at page 121(b):

[3] The first edition of Holinshed's *Chronicles* (2 vols.) was published in London by Lucas and John Harrison. They are classed as rare books. My partner, Arthur Haddaway, has a first edition in good condition. The date on the title page is 1577, but it appears that a license for sale of the books was not issued until 1578, and that date is sometimes given as the date of publication. *Encyclopaedia Britannica,* XI (1949 ed.), 640 (1957 ed.), 642. The first edition of the *Chronicles* contained many fine woodcuts, including one of Macbeth's meeting with the three witches. The woodcuts were not reproduced in any later edition. According to the *Dictionary of National Biography,* under Holinshed:

> The *Chronicles* form a very valuable repertory of historical information. The enormous number of authorities cited attests Holinshed's industry. The style is clear, although never elevated, and the chronicler fully justified his claim "to have an especial eye unto the truth of things," although his protestant bias is very marked throughout. . . . The Elizabethan dramatists drew many of their plots from Holinshed, and many of Shakespeare's historical plays [especially] *Macbeth, King Lear,* and parts of *Cymbeline* are based on Holinshed. At times (as in Henry IV) Shakespeare adopted not only Holinshed's facts, but some of his phrases.

Shakespeare's Holinshed, by W. G. Boswell-Stone, meticulously traces the use by Shakespeare of the *Chronicles* in his plays.

Hitherto have I spoken of weights, now it resteth that I do the like of such liquid measures as are presently used in Englande, and have been of old time amongst the Grecians and Romans, wherein I will deal so faithfully as I may, to the end this travail of mine may be some help to such as shall come after in conferring forren with our home made weights and measures, and for the better understanding of the histories, wherein such things are spoken of. The first therefore of our English measures, is:

A spoonful, which hath one of our drams and six grains.

An assay taste or sippet: 4 spoonfuls: or 4 drams and 24 grains.

A fardendele is a quarter of a pound, pint, or 3 ounces of troy.

A muytch, 6 ounces or half a pint.

A pint, 12 ounces or a pound or 4 fardendeles.

A quart, 24 ounces, 2 pints, or 2 pounds troy.

A pottle, 48 ounces or 4 pounds or so many pints.

A gallon, 96 ounces or 8 pounds or 8 pints.

A firkin, 8 gallons or 64 pounds, and this in ale, soap, and herring.

The kilderkin, 16 gallons.

The barrel, 32 gallons.

And these are our mere English liquid measures. The rest that we have are outlandish vessels, and such as are brought over unto us with wares from other countries. And yet we are not altogether guided by this rate (the more pity) but in some things several measures are used and received, as for example:

The firkin of beer hath 9 gallons.

The kilderkin, 18 gallons.

The barrel, 36.

As for the hogshead of beer it is lately come up, and because I see none made of this assize, but only the empty casks of wine reserved to this use, I pass over to say anything thereof. If it were according to the standard for beer, it should contain 72 gallons, which now hath but 64.

But of eels and salmon:

The firkin, 10 gallons and a half.

The half barrel, 21 gallons.

The barrel, 42 gallons.

The butt, 84 gallons.

Yet some statutes limit our eel measure in an equality unto that of herrings, of which 120 go to the hundred and 10,000 to the last, as they are commonly sold.

According to Holinshed, in 1577 the ordinary barrel, liquid measure, was 32 gallons, while the fish barrel was 42 gallons.

Other terms used in England for units of liquid measure are listed by Nicholson: noggin, jug, gill, jack, jock, joey, tuffet, strike, and comb. To all those named as liquid measures by Holinshed and Nicholson may be added these: bucket, quarter or seam, chaldron, load or wey, and last. They are a few of the "special measures of capacity" in the British system that are given in a handbook recently published by the United Nations.[4] The bucket is a liquid measure of four gallons; the others are shown to be terms for multiple bushels, 8 to 80.

I am inclined to believe that the inhabitants of the British Isles in the fifteenth and sixteenth centuries must have been obsessed with the coining of new terms for weights and measures, and, if there were quiz shows at that time, most of the questions that stumped the contestants must have been those asking for the meanings of such terms. Those who were familiar with Holinshed's *Chronicles* had an advantage.

In the sixteenth century, shopping for liquids or carrying on a conversation involving weights and measures in the British Isles must have been difficult without a dictionary or a glossary of terms. The use of terms with several meanings added further to the confusion. For instance, Holinshed refers to a 32-gallon barrel, a 36-gallon barrel, and a 42-gallon barrel in use in 1577.

The capacity of the barrel is not indicated in Shake-

[4] Statistical Office of the United Nations, *Worlds Weights and Measures, Handbook for Statisticians* (Provisional ed.), 11.

An early method of oil transportation, Oil City, Pa., 1864.

A barrel factory on Oil Creek, about 1860.

Flowing wells on the Tarr Farm.
Note the varied sizes of barrels shown.

Freight depot, Titusville, Pa., about 1864,
showing three different barrel sizes.

speare's *Henry VI* (Part 1, Act V, sc. iv., l. 57) (c. 1591),
where this interesting passage occurs:

> *"Place barrels of pitch upon the fatal stake,*
> *That so her torture may be shortened."*

Nor in the King James Version of the Bible of 1611, when
Elijah in I Kings asked the widow to bring him a morsel
of bread, and she replied:

> "I have not a cake, but an handful of meal in a barrel,
> and a little oil in a cruse."[5]

This language is from a subsequent verse:

> And the barrel of meal wasted not, neither did the
> cruse of oil fail.[6]

The same two verses, in the Revised Standard Version
of 1952, have a different translation, that removes speculation regarding the capacity of the "barrel":

> "I have nothing baked, only a handful of meal in a
> jar, and a little oil in a cruse."

and

> The jar of meal was not spent, neither did the cruse
> of oil fail.[7]

---

[5] 1 Kings XVII, 12.
[6] *Ibid.*, 16.
[7] *Encyclopedia Britannica* (1957 ed.), IV, 63, has an interesting article under the heading "Bread." It is said that breadmaking or the preparation of cakes from flour or parched
grains is one of the most ancient of human arts, that Abraham

No doubt the recent translation, changing "barrel" to "jar" is correct, but it is clear that "barrel" (a cask for liquids) was a common term at the turn of the seventeenth century when the King James Version was completed.

It is necessary to speculate about the capacity of the barrel in those days; however, there is no need to speculate about the prevalence of carelessness or sharp practices among brewers in Great Britain in the early part of the sixteenth century, for Henry VIII found that brewers of ale and beer were making their own barrels, usually of short measure. Therefore, a statute was passed that prohibited brewers from making barrels, and required them to use containers made by licensed coopers, who had to conform to standards prescribed under the law.[8] The statute, changed only by including letters that were omitted but indicated by commonly used symbols, reads in part as follows:

An acte that no Breuers of Bere or Ale shall make their barrels kylderkyns nor firkyns within them; and howmoche the same barrels &c. shall conteyne.

Where the Ale bruers and bere bruers of this Realme of England have used and dayly do use, for their owne singuler lucre profitte and gayne, to make

---

told his wife to make cakes (Genesis XVIII, 7), and that the ancient Egyptians carried the art of breadmaking to perfection.

[8] 23 Henry VIII c. IV (1531–32) in *Statutes of the Realm,* III, 366.

in their owne houses theyr barrels kylderkyns and firkyns of moche lasse quantitie contente rate and [assisse] than they ought to be, to the greate hurte prujudice and damage of the Kinges liege people and contrary to dyvers actes statutes auncient lawes and customes heretofore made hand and used, and to the distruccion of the pore crafte or mysterie of Cowpers: For reformacion whereof be it enacted by the King our Soveraigne Lorde the Lordes Spirituall and temporall and the Comons in this present parliament assembled and by auctoritie of the same, that noo bere bruer nor ale bruer that shall brue to sale bere or ale shall frome hensforth occupie by hym selff nor by any other to his use in his house nor elsewhere the misterie or crafte of Cowpers, nor make any barells kilderkyns fyrkyns or other vessels by hymselff nor by his or theyr owne servauntes, whereby they shall putt theyr bere or ale to sale; but that all such barrells kilderkins and other vessels of Wood, wherewith they shall putt their bere or ale to sale, shall from hensforth be made and marked accordingly as hereafter shall be expressed by the common artificers of Cowpers exercised and practised in the said occupacion; upon payne to forfaite and pay for every suche barrell kilderkyn firkyn or other vessell hereafter to be made contrarie to the tenour of this acte, three shillinges and foure pence. . . .

And be it further enacted by the said auctoritie that no bere brewer nor ale bruer, at any tyme after the feast of Lammas nowe nexte commyng, shall putt their bere or ale to sale to any personne or personnes to be spente and occupied within this Realme, in any other barrels kylderkyns firkyns or other vessells of woods other than shall be made and marked by an artificer of Coupers abovesaid; whereof every barrell for bere shall conteyn and hold xxxvj galons, every halffe barrell or kilderkyn xviij galons, and every firkyn ix galons . . . than is abovesaid, oneles he shall cause to be marked upon every suche vessell, that he shall so make of gretter and every barrell for ale shall conteyne xxxij galons, every kilderkyn xvj galons and every firkyn viij galons of full and juste measure or above and not under that measure.

Queen Anne's statute of 1707, referred to in the discussion of the gallon, also defined a barrel and other units of liquid measure. The effect is shown in this table:

1 wine gallon = 231 cubic inches

252 gallons = 1 tun

126 gallons = 1/2 of a tun = 1 butt or pipe

84 gallons = 1/3 of a tun = 1 puncheon

63 gallons = 1/2 of a butt or pipe = 1/4 of a tun = 1 hogshead

42 gallons = 1/2 of a puncheon or 1/6 of a tun = 1 tierce

31 1/2 gallons = 1/2 of a hogshead or 1/4 of a butt = 1 barrel

Histories of weights and measures establish, and the above table shows, that many units were derived by division. Terms or units such as "the half," "the third," and "the quarter" have been adopted in many countries. In the United States, we say "half" and "quarter" in connection with the dollar, and terms like "half a bushel" and "half a cord" are common.

John Quincy Adams, in his report on weights and measures, pointed out that one reason for the change in England—beginning in the reign of Edward III (1327–77)—from the 100-pound to the 112-pound hundredweight doubtless was to obtain a number that could be halved several times with a whole number resulting. Incidentally, sixteen is the base of the sexadecimal series and a favorite number because it may be divided by 2, 4, 8, and 16, or be halved four times and still produce a whole number. Such a division of any other base number that is not a multiple of 16 soon results in a fraction.

It is observed, from the table based on the statute of Richard III, that 63 gallons of wine was a hogshead, being one-half of a pipe, and that one-half of a hogshead or 31 1/2 gallons was a barrel, which was the capacity in gallons of a wine barrel in Queen Anne's reign and the capacity of a barrel for liquids generally used in this country by custom and by state statutes.

The old English statutes used the terms "puncheon" and "tierce." *Century Dictionary and Cyclopedia* says that "puncheon" is a word derived from Old French, and as a unit of measure was legalized in Great Britain in

1423 at 84 wine gallons. This quotation is then given in *Century* from "King Henry" (*Child's Ballads*, I, 149):

> *And he's sew'd up the bloody hide,*
> *A puncheon o'wine put in.*

Of interest here is not how the wine must have tasted, but the fact that "the half" of a "puncheon" is 42 gallons, called a "tierce," and the oil barrel, as a unit of measure, is 42 gallons.

The dictionaries say that "tierce" is an Old French word from the Latin "tertia," the feminine of "tertius," meaning a third, and that the "tierce" is one-third of a pipe (126 gallons) or 42 wine gallons. The term or measure "tierce" is not now in common use in the United States, but it was in Colonial days and much later. It was defined in a Massachusetts act of 1692, and a Pennsylvania act of about 1700 adopted the London "assize" for casks, with a "tierce" of 42 gallons. A "tierce" of 42 U. S. gallons is given as a unit of liquid measure in the United States in a book by John Henry Alexander, published in 1850, and one by F. W. Clark, published in 1875.[9]

A federal statute, passed in 1879 and still on the books, deals with "spirits, wines, and liquors, imported in pipes, hogsheads, *tierces*, barrels, casks, or other similar packages."[10]

[9] Alexander, *Universal Dictionary of Weights and Measures, Ancient and Modern, Reduced to Standards of the United States of America;* Clark, *Weights, Measures, and Monies of all Nations.*

Oscar A. Oldberg, in his book, *A Manual of Weights, Measures, and Specific Gravity,* published in 1885, gives information concerning units of liquid measure in the United States that can briefly be set forth as follows:

1 gallon wine = 231 cu. in.

1 gallon beer = 282 cu. in.

1 barrel wine = 7,276.5 cu. in = 31 plus wine gallons.

1 tierce wine = 9,702 cu. in. = 42 wine gallons.

1 barrel beer = 10,152 cu. in. = 36 beer gallons.

1 pipe wine = 29,106 cu. in. = 126 wine gallons.[11]

As late as 1899, this information concerning the situation in the United States appears in *Table of Weights and Measures,* by Thomas Egleston:

31 1/2 gallons wine = 1 barrel.

42 gallons wine = 1 tierce.

2 barrels wine = 1 hogshead.

2 hogshead wine = 1 pipe.

36 gallons beer = 1 barrel.[12]

Swanson argues, as already pointed out, that the story

[10] 20 Stats. 342, 19 United States Code (U.S.C.), Section 467.

[11] Page 9.

[12] Page 3.

of the 42-gallon barrel should not start with the gallon but with the ton. In a letter,[13] he gives his reasons, substantially as set forth in the next paragraph.

The ton was a cask of 252 gallons, used to determine the carrying capacity of ships. A ship of ten tons could carry in its hold the equivalent of ten casks of 252 gallons each. There was need for subdivisions, for obvious reasons—to fill out the corners and small spaces and simplify handling. So the ton had recognized subdivisions. There are many different barrels, but the reference here is to the salmon barrel and the herring barrel particularly, and to the wine barrel. The difference seems to have been the division of the ton into six or eight parts. Dividing 252 by 6 gives 42 gallons; dividing it by 8 gives 311/2 gallons. Barrels of 32 gallons are merely rounded out 311/2-gallon barrels. The act of Edward IV at Westminster on January 20, 1482, established the size of barrels for the packing of barreled fish. The barrel for salmon and eels was 42 gallons; that for herring 32 gallons. In the following year, another act (I Richard III, c. XIII), established the contents of vessels for wine and oil, in which the barrel contained 311/2 gallons. On March 5, 1816, the commissioners for the herring industry, having been empowered to fix the content or capacity of every measure, commonly called a "cran" (Scottish), by which fresh herrings, taken in the British herring industry, were to be bought and sold, set the capacity at 42 gallons English wine measure, and outlined the di-

[13] October 20, 1954.

mensions—the final part of the order reading, "The mean diameter will thus be twenty inches and one-fourth part of an inch, and the contents forty-two gallons and one half, but care will be taken at the adjustment of the measure and before it is branded, to reduce it to the exact gauge of forty-two gallons, by paring a little from the ends of the staves." Thus there was a 42-gallon barrel for salmon and eels, a 42-gallon "cran" for herrings, and a tierce, which was one-third of a pipe, or 42 gallons, not to be confused with a tertian, which was one-third of a ton. Thus, there was definitely a 42-gallon cask in use in England, and it was a divisible part of the ton, being one-sixth thereof.

There is no doubt that, long before 1700, there were casks of 42-gallon capacity in use in Great Britain, whether the gallon was 216 or 224 or 231 or 269 or some other number of cubic inches. Furthermore, there were units of measure and, doubtless, containers called barrels that varied in size with other variables, such as statutes changing the pound and the gallon, and the commodity involved, such as beer, wine, fish, oil, pork, or honey.

Beyond question, the word "barrel" has been used in the United States since Colonial days to describe a cask of cylindrical form, and as a measure of capacity for liquids.[14] However, as in Great Britain, statutes and cus-

[14] The Supreme Court of West Virginia, in its opinion filed in *Riggs* v. *Armstrong,* 23 W.Va. 760 (1885), gave these definitions of two classes of "oil-barrel" staves:

A first-class oil-barrel stave is one that is thirty-five

tom or usage brought about several meanings or variations, depending in part upon the commodity.

The Oil Barrel as a Container

IT IS TIME now to explore the main question: Why did the oil barrel in the United States, as a measure of capacity, mean 42 gallons of 231 cubic inches, instead of 31 1/2 (32), or 36, or 40, or 45 gallons, or some other standard? The point has already been made that there is no federal statute that defines a "barrel," except for a few commodities. There are, for instance, federal statutes defining a barrel for certain purposes for several com-

---

inches long, not less than four and one-half inches wide, three-fourths of an inch clear in thickness, and made of good white oak timber; and a second-class stave must have the same dimensions except that it may be of less width and not so easily worked, and may be rougher; so that it would take more staves and more work to make a barrel from staves of the second-class than from the first, and consequently they bring a less price in the market; but that both classes are merchantable and sold in the markets, and a barrel made from the one class sells for the same price as a barrel made from the other.

Unfortunately, it is not clear whether the oil barrel was for crude or refined oil. Not enough data are given for calculation of the number of gallons in a barrel made from the 35-inch staves.

modities, as for fruits, vegetables, lime, proof spirits (40 gallons to the barrel by a 1939 act), and fermented liquors (31 gallons to the barrel by a 1939 act), but there is no statute declaring that generally the barrel for liquids shall be 31 or 31 1/2 or 32 or any other number of gallons, or declaring that the crude-oil barrel shall be 42 gallons.

Probably because the barrel, unlike the gallon, is a variable unit, existing federal statutes imposing excise taxes on gasoline and lubricating oils and on imports of crude oil and derivatives place the tax on the gallon, not on the barrel.[1]

The birth of the oil industry in the United States is generally fixed as August, 1859, when the Seneca Oil Company, with Colonel Edwin L. Drake in charge of operations, drilled to a depth of about seventy feet and brought in a well (Drake's well) on Oil Creek, near Titusville in western Pennsylvania.[2] This makes apropos the statement that the first document showing oil in western Pennsylvania is thought to be a map printed more than one hundred years before the Drake well was drilled. The map, drawn by Lewis Evans, was printed

[1] Section 4521 of Internal Revenue Code of 1954.

[2] Paul H. Giddens, *The Birth of the Oil Industry,* gives an interesting account of the early period and the drilling of the Drake well; William H. Burns, "The Country's First Oil Company," *Our Sun,* Vol. XXI, No. 4 (Autumn, 1956), 37, tells about the first corporation that was organized to produce and sell "rock oil," and also about the drilling of the Drake well.

by Benjamin Franklin in 1755 and was reproduced in 1953 by the Ethyl Corporation as a service to the oil industry. It was the first map of the "Middle British Colonies," including what are now Virginia, West Virginia, Pennsylvania, Maryland, Ohio, and New York. The word "petroleum" appears in two places on the map, one near what is now Titusville, Pennsylvania. Beyond doubt, "petroleum" was placed on the map to show the location of oil seeps, long known to the Indians. These seeps near Titusville largely determined the location of the Drake well.[3]

Although, as mentioned in the preceding paragraph, the Drake well is generally considered to have constituted the beginning of the oil industry, Canadians now quickly protest when Americans take credit for giving birth to the industry in North America. A short sketch of the conflicting claims will be given, for they are interesting and provocative. Moreover, if Canada had developed a continuing, flourishing "oil industry," the unit for measuring crude oil would likely be the Imperial gallon, the 31 1/2-gallon barrel, or the metric ton.

[3] Only a few originals of the Lewis Evans map are known to exist. Fortunately, the Ethyl Corporation became the owner of one of them. The reproduction and a booklet giving interesting information about Lewis Evans and his map have been widely distributed among oilmen. John J. McLaurin, *Sketches in Crude Oil,* 29, mentions a map of the United States that was printed in England in 1787, in which "petroleum" is marked in two places, one on Oil Creek. It is logical to think that the reference was to the Lewis Evans map or to a map based in part on the Evans Map.

It must be admitted that the Canadians have proof that James M. Williams, as early as 1857, dug "with pick and shovel," according to one account,[4] producing oil

[4] *Derrick's Hand Book of Petroleum,* I, 1018–19, in the biography of Colonel Ferris. It is said that Colonel Ferris went to Canada in October, 1858, to see the Williams' wells, and bought some crude oil from Williams. The account in the books of Colonel Ferris shows that he paid Williams $100 for the oil (quantity not given) and $285 to the United States as duty.

The several volumes of Derrick's handbook are considered to be a prime source of information about the petroleum industry, especially in western Pennsylvania for the period 1859 to 1900. The Derrick Publishing Company of Oil City, Pennsylvania, in 1884, published a handbook (booklet) that gave considerable information, some of it in chronological form, about the petroleum industry. Edward B. Swanson has obtained one for the petroleum section in the library of the Department of the Interior. They are hard to find.

That handbook was the beginning of a more elaborate program, for, in the late 1800's, the Derrick Publishing Company undertook the difficult task of publishing in multiple volumes a more comprehensive chronological history of the petroleum industry. Books, periodicals, newspapers, and other sources of information were checked. Old-timers were interviewed, and records (public and private) were examined. The first volume, containing more than 1,000 pages, was published in 1898. It contains, in chronological order, almost a day to day account of interesting items and events that took place; there are many pages of statistics, such as for production, prices, and exports; there is a section with pictures of the outstanding oilmen of the time, with a short biography of each; and, finally, there are advertisements by refiners and equipment firms.

The second volume of 573 pages is similar. It was pub-

wells in gum beds in Lambton County, Ontario, south-
east of Sarnia, and that by 1860 a considerable number
of wells were in operation near the town of Oil Springs,
which is said to have been a boom town of 1,600, perhaps
3,000, with twelve general stores and nine hotels.[5] No
saloons are mentioned.

---

lished in 1900, covering the years 1898 and 1899. The program then lost its vigor. Volume III, a paperback of eighty-six
pages, covers the years 1900 through 1915, and Volume IV, a
paperback of sixty-one pages, covers the years 1916 through
1919. These were followed by annual reviews of about twenty
pages each for the years 1920 through 1926. All of this material is invaluable to the historian seeking information about
the earlier days of the industry, and the information appears
to be sufficiently accurate to be relied upon for most purposes,
without undertaking to seek out the original sources.

For brevity, the first volume will be cited as follows: *Derrick's Hand Book*, I.

[5] It is clear that the development of oil at or near Oil
Springs furnished facts that were used in the three-volume
novel, *The Golden Butterfly*, by Sir Walter Besant and James
Rice, published in London in 1876 by Tinsley Brothers. In
the novel, one of the main characters made a great fortune
by developing an oil field in Ontario that was located in
a bog called "gum beds." The title pages of *The Golden Butterfly* (three-volume edition) do not show the names of the
authors other than by saying that the novel is "By the authors of 'Ready-Money Mortiboy,' 'This Son of Vulcan'" and
others. They were Besant and Rice. The *Encyclopaedia Britannica* (1911 edition), under Sir Walter Besant, correctly
gives the date of publication as 1876; however, the 1949 and
1957 editions erroneously give the publication date as 1871,
an error that is not made in the biographical sketch of James
Rice. A small (4 1/2x6 1/4 inches) one-volume edition was

Arguments and facts bearing on whether Drake or Williams (who was born in the United States) may properly be called the father of the oil industry are given in an article, "North America's Father of Oil," by Fergus Cronin, found in the magazine, *Imperial Oil Review*, for April, 1955,[6] in the Fort Worth *Star-Telegram* for October 23, 1955,[7] and in an amusing article, "Just Who Did Start This Oil Business Anyway," appearing in a magazine published in 1956 by the Sun Oil Company.[8]

The Canadians are warned that, if they continue to claim Canada as the place of birth of the oil industry, even in North America, they will be reminded that evidence is available to show the widespread medicinal use by the Seneca Indians long before 1850 of oil from seeps in what is now Pennsylvania.[9]

published by Collins' Clear Type Press. The date is not given. There is a dedication, absent in the three-volume edition, declaring that *The Golden Butterfly* was first published in the newspaper "World." There is a preface by the authors, also absent in the three-volume edition, that is dated March, 1877. The publication date of the one-volume edition was either 1876 or 1877. I have both editions.

[6] Published by Imperial Oil Company.

[7] Section 3, p. 1.

[8] *Our Sun* (Winter, 1956), 22.

[9] Simon W. Freese of Fort Worth has called my attention to a passage in the book by Washington Irving, entitled *The Adventures of Captain Bonneville, U.S.A., in the Rocky Mountains and the Far West,* in which an account is given of the medicinal use of oil in the Wyoming area at least as early as 1800. The book is based on talks with Captain Bonneville and a study of his voluminous records. The Captain

If that was not the birth of the oil industry, at least in North America, then the United States' claim to pri-

began his explorations in May, 1832. This account is given of some of his experiences while in the area of the Wind River Mountains, Wyoming:

> In this neighborhood, the captain made search for the "Great Tar Spring," one of the wonders of the mountains; the medicinal properties of which, he had heard extravagantly lauded by the trappers. After a toilsome search, he found it at the foot of a sand-bluff, a little to the east of the Wind River Mountains; where it exuded in a small stream of the color and consistency of tar. The men immediately hastened to collect a quantity of it to use as an ointment for the galled backs of their horses, and as a balsam for their own pains and aches. From the description given of it, it is evidently the bituminous oil called petroleum or naptha, which forms a principal ingredient in the potent medicine called British Oil. It is found in various parts of Europe and Asia, in several of the West India islands, and in some places of the United States. In the State of New York, it is called Seneca Oil, from being found near the Seneca Lake.

The account is found at page 286 in the author's revised edition, published by G. P. Putnam and Sons in 1869, and at page 142 of the book as published by John B. Alden in 1885.

What is thought to be the first reliable scientific record of the early discovery and use of oil in the United States is the account by Professor Benjamin Silliman, published in 1833 in *The American Journal of Science*. A quotation from his account appears at pages 127–32 of Crew's, *Practical Treatise on Petroleum*. He tells of the seeps in New York and in Western Pennsylvania and the use of oil "by the people of the vicinity for sprains and rheumatism and for sores upon their horses."

ority can fairly be based on the recovery and sale of crude oil and products in considerable quantities as early as 1849, as the following account will show.

A flourishing business in Pennsylvania in the 1850's, and even earlier, involved the drilling of wells for brine to be used in making salt. Some of the wells were drilled to a depth of at least four hundred feet; a few of them near Tarentum not only produced salt but a considerable quantity of crude oil, first considered to be a nuisance. One such well was owned by Thomas Kier, the father of Samuel M. Kier; another, near the Kier well, was owned by Lewis Peterson, Sr. The Kiers also leased a tract from Peterson on which there were several wells that produced oil along with the brine. Samuel Kier, an ingenious man, doubtless remembering that the Seneca Indians and others had used crude oil for medicinal purposes, developed a thriving business by bottling the oil obtained from brine wells and selling it as a medicine under the name "Kier's Petroleum, or Rock Oil." It was also known as "Seneca Oil." The claims about its efficiency were broad; doubtless, so broad, if made now, as to violate the Pure Food and Drug Act and to occasion the disapproval of the Federal Trade Commission. Here is an example of the claims made in one circular:

Kier's Petroleum, or Rock Oil, Celebrated for its Wonderful Curative Powers. A Natural Remedy! Procured from a Well in Allegheny Co., Pa., Four-Hundred Feet below the Earth's Surface. Put up and Sold by Samuel M. Kier, 363 Liberty Street, Pittsburgh, Pa.

The healthful balm, from Nature's secret spring,
The bloom of health and life to man will bring;
As from her depths this magic liquid flows
To calm our sufferings and assuage our woes.

The Petroleum has been fully tested! It was placed before the public as A REMEDY OF WONDER-FUL EFFICACY. Every one not acquainted with its virtues doubted its healing qualitie. The cry of humbug was raised against it. It had some friends— those who were cured through its wonderful agency. Those spoke in its favor. The lame through its in-strumentality were made to walk—the blind to see. Those who had suffered for years under the tortur-ing pains of RHEUMATISM, GOUT AND NEU-RALGIA were restored to health and usefulness. Several who were blind were made to see. If you still have doubts, go and ask those who have been cured! . . . We have the witnesses, crowds of them, who will testify in terms stronger than we can write them to the efficacy of this remedy; cases abandoned by physicians of unquestionable celebrity have been made to exclaim, "THIS IS THE MOST WONDER-FUL REMEDY YET DISCOVERED!" Its tran-scendent power to heal MUST and WILL become known and appreciated. . . . The Petroleum is a Natural Remedy; it is put up as it flows from the bosom of the earth, without anything being added to or taken from it. It gets its ingredients from the beds of substances which it passes over in its secret channel. They are blended together in such a way as to defy all human competition. . . . Petroleum will continue to be used and applied as a Remedy as long as man continues to be afflicted with disease. Its discovery is a new era in medicine.[10]

Samuel Kier, at least by 1850, was also engaged in distilling or refining crude oil to be used as an illuminant, as was Colonel A. C. Ferris, of New York. That was before the Canadian, Williams, carried on refining operations. Samuel Kier not only was a pioneer oil refiner but also made improvements in the camphene lamp, so that it would burn without smoking and give a brilliant light, thus creating a better market for "carbon oil," as it was called.[11] Colonel Ferris, also a pioneer refiner, made ex-

[10] McLaurin, *Sketches in Crude Oil,* 29. Another circular, which made even stronger claims, is quoted in *Derrick's Hand Book,* I, 949.

[11] The Kier story in considerable detail is found in several books, among which are Giddens, *The Birth of the Oil Industry,* 23–25; *Pennsylvania Petroleum 1750–1872,* 10ff.; McLaurin, *Sketches in Crude Oil,* 29. In *Derrick's Hand Book,* I, beginning at page 947, is a rather complete biographical sketch of Samuel Kier. A recent article is Burns, "The Country's First Oil Company," *Our Sun,* XXI, No. 4 (Autumn, 1956), 37. It is not too clear whether Kier or Ferris first used the term "carbon oil." Giddens, *The Birth of the Oil Industry,* 25, gives credit to Ferris. Without trying to settle who first gave the name "carbon oil" to refined oil, it can be said that a Pennsylvania appellate court in *Kier* v. *Peterson* (1862), shortly to be discussed in the text, referred to crude oil as "carbon oil." From other sources, it would appear that Kier,

cellent lamp oil and did a considerable marketing business in lamps and lamp oil before Williams found a market for his oil or undertook to refine it. Indeed, it appears that Ferris went to Canada in 1858 and made a tour of the oil area with Williams; he bought one hundred dollars' worth of crude oil from Williams—the first sale made by Williams—and he told Williams that the oil would be refined and marketed.[12] It is implied, and with logic, that Williams got the idea of refining crude oil from Ferris.

What is considered to be the first lawsuit over petroleum to reach an appellate court in the United States was an action by Lewis Peterson against Thomas and Samuel M. Kier. According to the opinion by the Pennsylvania appellate court, Peterson executed a lease of land to the Kiers dated October 30, 1837, authorizing the lessees to drill and produce brine for the manufacture of salt. Several wells were operated, and oil, called in the opinion of the court "carbon oil or petroleum," "petroleum or rock oil," "petroleum or mineral oil," and "petroleum," was produced with the brine. The Kiers separated the oil from the brine and either sold or utilized it. Peterson sued to recover $20,000, as the value of 50,000 gallons of oil, asserting that the lease covered only brine

Ferris, and the judge who wrote the opinion in the Kier-Peterson case adopted the term "carbon oil" that was in common use.

[12] *Derrick's Hand Book*, I, 1018–19, in the biography of Ferris has an account of Ferris's trip to Canada.

and that the Kiers did not get title to the oil. The court held in favor of the Kiers, saying that the lessees had title to the oil and could let it run to waste or could market it. One judge dissented, saying that perhaps the lessees were not bound to preserve the oil, but, having done so, it belonged to the lessor.[13] In any event, Kier was producing oil, along with brine, and was doing a flourishing marketing business with oil long before 1857.

Should the Canadians, in spite of the evidence to the contrary, still contend that the oil industry was born in Canada in 1857, or before the Drake well was drilled in 1859, additional refutation will be given. If production, refining, use, and marketing of petroleum (including

[13] *Kier* v. *Peterson*, 41 Pa. St. (5 Wright) 357 (1862). These cases by appellate courts bear on the same subject: *Kitchen* v. *Smith*, 101 Pa. St. (5 Outerbridge) 452, 457–58 (1882), in which one of the judges took the opportunity to say that he thought that the dissenting opinion in the Kier-Peterson case should have been the opinion of the court; *Truby* v. *Palmer*, 3 Pa. St. 156, 6 Atl. 74 (1886); *Allen* v. *Palmer*, 136 Pa. St. 556, 26 Atl. 516 (1890); *Wood County Pet. Co.* v. *West Virginia Co.*, 28 W.Va. 210, 57 Am.Rep. 659 (1886); *Stroud* v. *Guffey*, 3 S.W.2d 592 (Tex. Civ. App.), 16 S.W.2d 527 (1929, Comm. of App.), 64 A.L.R. 730, with annotations; *Stradley* v. *Magnolia Pet. Co.*, 155 S.W.2d 649 (Tex. Civ. App. 1941, writ refused); *Borys* v. *Canadian Pacific Ry. Co. et al.*, 4 W.W.R. (N.S.) 481, 1 Oil & Gas Reporter 605 (Alberta Supreme Court 1952), affirmed by Privy Council, I All E.R. 451, 2 Oil & Gas Reporter 1597 (1953). The Borys case involved the question whether a deed, with an exception or reservation of "petroleum," excepted "oil and gas" or only "oil," but not "gas." The holding was that only oil was excepted.

bitumens, asphalt, oil, and gas) in considerable quantity
constitute an industry, then the oil or petroleum industry
was given birth in ancient times, even before the birth
of Christ, for bituminous material was used extensively
in ancient days for many purposes, such as building material, waterproofing, calking of ships, road building, il-
lumination, medicine, fire, and, for a time, in mummifi-
cation.[14]

There is proof that the Chinese, as early as one thousand years ago, had drilled wells for oil and gas to a
depth of 3,000 or more feet, using bronze bits and casing
the holes with bamboo. The oil or gas produced was used
for heating and lighting.[15]

Surely the facts justify the conclusion that the birth-

[14] Information on the use of bitumens in ancient times is
given in various books, but in great detail in *Bitumen and
Petroleum in Antiquity* by R. J. Forbes. What may be called
a second edition of that book appears as the first section of
Volume I of *Studies in Ancient Technology*, published by
E. J. Brill in 1955 in Leiden, Netherlands. E. DeGolyer, of
DeGolyer and MacNaughton, used as a Christmas gift in 1946
a booklet, *The Antiquity of the Oil Industry, With Copious
Notes and References by the Author* (DeGolyer), in which,
after amusing comments and show of scholarly research (such
as footnotes), he concluded that Job was the first oilman.
Reproduction of several old woodcuts, one showing use of a
"doodle-bug," found in a book published in 1556, and another
from a book printed in 1491 depicting "petroleum" flowing
from an aperture in rocks into a jar, add to the interest and
value of the booklet.

[15] Forbes, *Bitumen and Petroleum in Antiquity*, 11; John G.
Swindell and George R. Burnell, *Wells and Well-Sinking*, 2.

place of the petroleum industry in North America is the United States, not Canada, and that is one reason why the Imperial gallon or the metric ton did not become the standard in the United States.

Whatever may be the decision regarding the correct date for the birth of the oil industry in North America and the country which fathered it, there is no doubt that the completion of the Drake well started a drilling campaign that quickly spread to near-by areas, with the result that in the 1860's large quantities of oil were produced and utilized. The problems attending the handling, storing, and transporting of the oil were formidable. The fields were not on the railroad lines, as so often happens; consequently, the oil was placed in casks and loaded in wagons. The roads were few and inadequate for the heavy traffic that developed, and the demand for casks became almost insatiable. The country was scoured for suitable containers, usually called barrels, regardless of size. Every conceivable type of receptacle was used, especially fairly large casks or barrels, including nail kegs and washtubs, according to one account. It is logical to think that great efforts were made to get "tight" barrels or containers that had held liquids such as wine, whiskey, cider, vinegar, beer, and salt, or that had held fish with accompanying liquids.[16] As far as containers

[16] *Derrick's Hand Book*, I, 20ff. (for the years from 1860 to 1865); McLaurin, *Sketches in Crude Oil*, Chapter XV; John T. Flynn, *God's Gold*, 94; Herbert Asbury, *The Golden Flood*, 138; Edmund Morris, *Derrick and Drill*, 38.

were concerned, tightness rather than capacity was sought, although preference must have been given, even in the first few years, to fairly large "barrels" which could still be easily handled by one or two men.

Price quotations and production figures on oil were usually given in gallons in the early 1860's, and when they were given in barrels, there was infrequent reference to the size of the barrel or to the number of gallons to the barrel.

It does appear, however, that a barrel of 40 gallons was frequently used. Thomas A. Gale consistently referred to a 40-gallon barrel in his book, *The Wonder of the Nineteenth Century; Rock Oil in Pennsylvania and Elsewhere,* published in 1860, less than a year after the Drake well was drilled. The preface is dated June 1, 1860.[17] It is considered to be the first book about the oil fields in Pennsylvania, and it is a most interesting one. Only three copies are known to exist: one in the Huntington Library at San Marino, California, one in the library of Columbia University, and the third in the possession of the Ethyl Corporation, New York. That company in 1952 printed a limited number of facsimiles, so that the interesting item would be available to historians and members of the petroleum industry. The original book is a small paperback of eighty pages, small print, published in 1860 by Sloan & Griffeth of Erie, Pennsylvania. As yet, no information about the author has

[17] See pages 35, 58, and 59 for reference to a forty-gallon barrel.

been found. Evidently, he was a man of education and careful in his research, for he did an excellent job of reporting the facts and conditions and of forecasting a wide use of "rock oil" in medicines and paints, as fuel for ships, locomotives, and boilers, and generally for light and fuel. The Ethyl Corporation supplemented the facsimile of the Gale book by a booklet of interesting explanatory notes.[18]

Although a number of writers referred to a 40-gallon barrel in recounting the early days of the oil industry,[19] little has been found to establish the origin of such a

[18] Ernest C. Miller, of the West Penn Oil Company, Warren, Pa., did most of the research for the notes, while Paul H. Giddens, now president of Hamline University, St. Paul, and the late E. DeGolyer, gave advice during their preparation. A brief account of the Gale book is given in "Petroleum's First Book," *Ethyl News* (September–October, 1957), 18.

[19] *Derrick's Hand Book,* I, 16, 25, 706; Morris, *Derrick and Drill,* 33, 132, 243. The name of the author is not given in the book, but he is declared to be the author of *Ten Acres Enough* and is thereby identified as Edmund Morris. Material from the *Venango Spectator* of November 5, 1862, and the *Pittsburgh Evening Chronicle* of August 19, 1864, on the forty-gallon barrel, is reproduced in Giddens, *Pennsylvania Petroleum 1750–1872, A Documentary History,* 224–25; Henry Erni, *Coal, Oil and Petroleum,* 183–85; Rev. S. J. M. Eaton, *Petroleum: A History of the Oil Regions of Venango County, Pennsylvania,* 288; Raymond F. Bacon and William A. Hamor, *TheAmerican Petroleum Industry,* 244; S. F. Peckham, "Report Upon the Production, Technology, and Uses of Petroleum and Its Products," 92, 98, 106, 107, 109, 151; and W. M. Dunham, in Dorsey Hager, *Oil-Field Practice; Baroid News Bulletin* (March–April, 1955), 28.

barrel or measure. However, it is reasonably clear that, as a unit of liquid measure, it was in fairly common use in western Pennsylvania during the middle of the nineteenth century. This is odd, inasmuch as a Pennsylvania statute approved April 15, 1834, and still on the books in 1956, declared that 31 1/2 gallons made one barrel,[20] thus making legal a unit of liquid capacity that had long been a general standard in Great Britain and the United States.

The digest of state statutes found in the Adams' Report, already discussed, shows that several, prior to 1821, had defined a barrel for liquids as containing 31 1/2 gallons. The only statute providing for a 40-gallon barrel was passed in Virginia. In that state, an early act (1631–32) declared that a barrel of corn was five bushels Winchester measure, 40 gallons to the barrel, while an act of 1795 declared that a barrel of salt was five bushels, the equal of 40 wine gallons. It is suggested that perhaps the long-time use of a 40-gallon barrel in Virginia, at least as a unit of measure, may have been the origin of the 40-gallon barrel in western Pennsylvania in the early days of the oil industry. Adams also reported statutes in Pennsylvania and Massachusetts providing for a "tierce" of 42 gallons and a Maryland statute stating that the "tierce" should contain not less than 45 gallons, but the probable influence of these statutes is not clear.

It is not difficult to think of many problems that arose

[20] *Federal and State Weights and Measures Laws Through 1949 Amendments*, 845, Sec. 43.

in Drake's time from the lack of "tight" containers or barrels and from the great variations in sizes, especially after the barrel began to supplant the gallon as a unit of measure. The following quotation gives a good account of the situation:

A. W. Smiley, one of the famous pioneers of the industry, laughingly confessed at a reunion of old-timers that he had once bought 100 barrels of oil and had sent his teamster up with some rather generously-sized containers. The next day a man stormed into his office and demanded if he was the one to whom the irate one had sold the oil.

"Yes," replied Smiley, "and my man says you won't deliver it."

"What do you take me for, anyway?" demanded the other. "If you think I am going to deliver 60 or 70 gallons of oil to every barrel, you're badly mistaken. Every barrel of that oil cost me a thousand dollars, and I won't stand this robbery!"

So they compromised.

L. H. Smith, the gentleman in question, happened to be present when this recital was given, and could not resist making a reply.

"The story is all right," he conceded, "except for the barrels. What he sent up were good-sized casks. Why, even the teamster remarked, when he saw a 250-barrel tank on my farm there, "If Smiley were here," said he, "he'd put a head in that tank and call it a barrel!"[21]

[21] *The Lamp,* Vol. XV, No. 3 (October, 1932), 8; appears

Some of the casks or barrels were big, and some were small; some were "tight," and some leaked badly. Moreover, the demand was almost never filled, and prices were high, in spite of large shipments of old and new containers from distant states and the increase in barrel production in Pennsylvania and elsewhere.[22]

As far as this discussion is concerned, "barrel" has a double meaning: (1) a cask, cylindrical in form, flat at both ends, bulging in the middle, and of a size capable

---

also in *Oil and Gas Journal*, Vol. XXXII, No. 26 (November 16, 1933), 65. Smiley is the author of the book, *A Few Scraps (Oily and Otherwise)*.

[22] Eaton, *A History of the Oil Regions of Venango County, Pennsylvania*, 280; W. M. Dunham, in Hager, *Oil Field Practice*, 269; *The Lamp*, Vol. XV, No. 3 (October, 1932), 7; *Oil and Gas Journal*, Vol. XXXII, No. 26 (November 16, 1933), 65; Asbury, *The Golden Flood*, Chapter V; testimony of Patrick C. Boyle on September 6, 1899, reported in Volume I of *Report of Industrial Commission*, 407ff.; *Derrick's Hand Book*, I, for the years 1862 and 1863, showing demand and prices, with the prices in 1863 as high as $3.25 for a new barrel; Flynn, *God's Gold*, 94, telling of Rockefeller's visit to Oil City in 1860, the need for barrels, and the manufacture of barrels by Brewer and Watson, sawmill men, and by George H. Bissell, who was partially responsible for the drilling of the Drake well. Giddens, *DuPont Magazine*, Vol. XLVI, No. 5 (October–November, 1952), 8–10, tells an interesting story of the oil barrel. It has the title "When the Oil Barrel was King" and is illustrated with a number of old photographs. A recent and excellent article, "The Barrel That Isn't," by Dorothy F. Garretson, appears in *Our Sun*, Vol. XIX, No. 3 (Summer, 1954), 16–17. The illustrations by Raymond Shockley are amusing as well as instructive.

of holding a fairly large number of gallons, such as 30 to 60; and (2) a measure of liquid capacity of a specified number of gallons. Smiley correctly said that, in the early 1860's, a barrel of oil usually meant a cask of oil, regardless of its size, for there was no standard size in use. However, the word "barrel" was also frequently used as a unit of liquid measure, especially with respect to estimates and reports of production, or in calculating quantity of oil in bulk. There is considerable evidence to justify the conclusion that, until about 1867, the term "barrel," when used as a unit of liquid measure, meant a container holding 40 gallons. However, nothing has yet been found to indicate that casks of 40-gallon capacity were manufactured and were generally available.

The United States government added to the confusion by the act of March 3, 1865, which imposed on "crude petroleum or rock oil that might be produced and sold . . . a duty of one dollar on each and every barrel of not more than forty-five gallons . . . provided further that when casks, barrels, or other vessels are used, holding more than 45 gallons, the excess shall be paid for at the rate of $1.00 for every 45 gallons."[23] Conceivably, Congress was aware of the Maryland statute providing that a "tierce" should contain at least 45 gallons. Undoubtedly, Congress had been informed of the use of containers (barrels) of various sizes and undertook to impose a tax of one dollar on each barrel that held no more than 45 gallons, whether it was a 31 1/2-gallon barrel, a

[23] 13 Stat. 484.

40-gallon barrel, a 42-gallon barrel, or a 45-gallon barrel.

Regardless of why Congress adopted a method of taxation that virtually fixed a barrel at 45 gallons, the tax was indeed a stiff one, and it is interesting to read the many items in *Derrick's Hand Book* that tell about oilmen going to Washington to protest the tax and to obtain repeal. The arguments must have been valid or the pressure great, for the tax on crude oil was removed in 1866.[24]

In connection with the heavy federal tax on oil and products under the act of 1865, a special committee of the United States Revenue Commission was appointed to study oil as a source of revenue. The commission filed its report, dated February, 1866, giving much information on conditions in the oil fields, costs, production, values, and the like. Although the act of 1865 imposed a duty of $1.00 on every barrel of not more than 45 gallons, it is odd that the report of the committee used a 40-gallon barrel in discussing such things as production, prices, and exports.[25] No reason is given, but the action of the committee is strong proof of the common use of a barrel of 40 gallons as a unit of measure as late as February, 1866.

Starting with the assumption that containers for transportation of oil, especially for foreign trade, had to be of a size fractional to a ton of 252 gallons to conform to prescribed weights and measures, Edward B. Swanson offers this argument in support of the adoption of a 42-

[24] 30 Cong., 1 sess., *Joint Resolution No. 35*, 15 Stat. 355.
[25] Special Report No. 7 of the United States Revenue Commission.

66

gallon barrel as a standard container: There was a choice among three containers: a hogshead of 63 gallons (1/4 of a ton), that weighed, with contents, about 500 pounds, and was thus probably too heavy to handle easily; a barrel of 31 1/2 gallons (1/8 of a ton), that weighed, with contents, about 250 pounds, and thus was probably too small in terms of contents in relation to the cost of the container and its handling; and the tierce of 42 gallons (1/6 of a ton), that weighed, with contents, about 335 pounds, and thus was a size that could be easily handled by a man at each end and had a reasonable relation to the cost of the container and handling.

The Swanson logic is excellent, although little evidence has been submitted, and none has been found by me, to indicate that the barrel makers, producers, purchasers, or transporters of the 1860's followed such reasoning in deciding on the size of a barrel to manufacture or on the unit of measure.

There is, however, some evidence that a tight 42-gallon barrel was sometimes used, at least for refined oil, in some parts of Pennsylvania about 1866. This evidence is found in the opinion of the Supreme Court of Massachusetts in the case of *Miller* v. *Stevens,* decided in 1868.[26] All the facts are not clearly stated in the opinion, but it appears that a contract was made for the sale of one thousand barrels of refined Pennsylvania oil; the purchaser refused to accept delivery, so the seller sued for the contract price. The contract did not make clear

[26] 100 Mass. 518, 97 Am.Dec. 123 (1868).

whether the term "barrels" was used to describe a quantity or merely vessels or containers of a certain kind and capacity. Because of the ambiguity, the court permitted evidence to show the sense in which the word "barrels" was used. The evidence established that refined oil was often sold in barrels and that the usual size was 42 gallons. The court held that the Pennsylvania statute prescribing the number of gallons to a barrel as a liquid measure (31 1/2 gallons) did not apply "to sales by kegs, casks, or vessels of a particular kind"; that the barrels that the seller offered for exhibit and sale were of 42-gallon capacity; that, in all discussions between the parties, no question was raised that the barrels offered were not what the contract required, if the oil was of the requisite fire test; and that the intention was to use the word "barrel" as a specific article of commerce, not as a statutory measure of quantity.

The evidence in the Miller-Stevens case is not considered to constitute proof that the 42-gallon barrel, either as a container or unit of measure, was in common use in the oil fields of Pennsylvania as early as 1866. Other evidence leads to a contrary conclusion.

An article in the *Oil and Gas Journal* of April 15, 1921, gives in positive language an account of the origin of the 42-gallon oil barrel. The article is frequently cited as settling the question of origin or why such a unit of measure was adopted. In part, it reads:

According to an oil historian, early oil barrels were

Nelly Bly

From Ernest C. Miller, **Oil Mania.**

Ben Hogan
Sketched by Elton Davis.

of various sizes. When crude oil was discovered in Pennsylvania in 1859, barrels commonly used for wine, beer, whiskey, cider, and other liquids were utilized by oil men as containers for their product. ...

In 1864–65 the first standard barrel was made by Samuel Van Syckle, at Miller Farm, near Titusville, Pa. It was of 42 gallons capacity, the size fixed in the year 1461 in England for the herring barrel, during the reign of Edward IV.

Van Syckle specified the size of the staves to be used and made an honest 42-gallon barrel. Almost immediately he had practically a monopoly of the business, and the odd size barrels gradually disappeared.

The present system of gauging oil tanks was started in 1865 when F. E. Hammond, of Miller Farm, Pa., was asked if he could figure the amount of oil contained in each vertical foot of certain oil tanks. In a few days Hammond prepared a table of one of these tanks, showing the amount of oil it would hold per inch from bottom to top, based on a measurement of 42 gallons to the barrel. Hammond's table come [came] into general use and this method of measuring tanks never has changed.[27]

Commenting first on the last paragraph, there is some question whether the table was based on a 42- or a 44-gallon barrel. Alfred W. Smiley, an oil historian of the period, also gives credit to F. E. Hammond for making,

---

[27] "Forty-two Gallon Barrel Adopted at Miller Farm," 62.

in 1865, the first tank table, but Smiley wrote, "The table was scaled at forty-four gallons for a barrel."[28]

A search through *Derrick's Hand Book* and other books and accounts of the period fails to reveal anything to confirm the statement in the *Oil and Gas Journal* that Samuel Van Syckle engaged in the manufacture of barrels or that anyone else made such a fine barrel that it became a standard product in great demand and thereby fixed the unit of measure at 42 gallons. This is not to say that Van Syckle did not manufacture or participate with others in the manufacturing of first-class 42-gallon barrels, for Van Syckle was an able, foresighted man. It is to say that no evidence has been found to support the story in the *Oil and Gas Journal* that Van Syckle may properly be called the father of the 42-gallon oil barrel.

Miss A. Violet Dubar, of the staff of the Drake Museum, Titusville, at the request of Edward B. Swanson, checked newspapers and other source material but was unable to find any reference to barrel-making by Van Syckle. Surely, the story would have been news if Van Syckle had a "monopoly" that existed because he made the best and the standard barrel.

It is true that good barrels were hard to get and were at times expensive, and that the heavy costs and many difficulties, especially with teamsters, incident to the transportation of barrels of oil in wagons caused Van Syckle in 1865 to build what is considered to be the first long-distance crude-oil pipe line; a five-mile line, two

[28] *A Few Scraps (Oily and Otherwise)*, 142–43.

inches in diameter.[29] The Van Syckle line was the beginning of pipe-line transportation and, combined with construction of railroads to the fields and the use of tank cars, brought about a rather rapid displacement of transportation by wagons and, to a considerable extent, of transportation by rafts, especially the "pond-freshets" method. In the latter method of transportation, dams were built across a stream, creating ponds; rafts and flat-bottomed boats filled with barrels of oil remained in the ponds during low water; when heavy rains came, filling the pools, the dams were cut, and, in great confusion, the rafts and other water carriers were started down the stream.[30] Such a method of transportation was spectacular but hardly satisfactory, as it resulted in great losses from collisions and fires. It soon gave way to more modern means.

Pipe lines and oil tank cars gradually lessened the

[29] A good account of the building of the line, the efforts of the teamsters to destroy it, and the fight between Van Syckle and Martin Bryan, the burley leader of the teamsters, is given in Harry Botsford, "The Pipe Line War—Brief and Decisive," *Service* (July, 1956). *Service* is the magazine of Cities Service. See also Botsford, *The Valley of Oil*, 168–77. For the point of view of the teamsters, see Joseph Millard, *The Wickedest Man*, 95.

[30] Eaton, *Petroleum: The History of the Oil Regions of Venango County, Pennsylvania*, Chapter XII; McLaurin, *Sketches in Crude Oil*, Chapter XI; Giddens, *The Birth of the Oil Industry*, Chapter VIII; Asbury, *The Golden Flood*, Chapter V; Botsford, *The Valley of Oil*, Chapter XVII. Each gives a colorful account of transportation of oil in the 1860's.

need for barrels; consequently, if Van Syckle manufactured such good barrels that he acquired a monopoly, he virtually put himself out of that business when he proved that oil could be cheaply transported long distances by pipe line.

A number of writers and "old-timers" have concluded that an agreement of oil operators in 1866 is the most likely origin of the 42-gallon oil barrel, at least as a unit of measure.[31] In *Derrick's Hand Book* (I, 77), the following account appears as an item of interest for August 31, 1866, and it is often pointed out as relating the true origin of the 42-gallon oil barrel:

At Oil Rock, five miles north of Burning Springs, West Virginia, the Orchard well completed, and started to pumping at the rate of 600 bbls. per day; oil was developed at a depth of 200 feet, and the

[31] *The Lamp*, Vol. XV, No. 3 (October, 1932), 7, and the 75th Anniversary Edition (1957), 16; testimony of Patrick C. Boyle, in *Report of Industrial Commission;* Charles Morrow Wilson, *Oil Across the World*, 77; Asbury, *The Golden Flood*, 138ff.; *Oil and Gas Journal*, Vol. XXXII, No. 26 (November 16, 1933), 65; Garretson, *Our Sun*, Vol. XIX, No. 3 (Summer, 1954), 16. Lalia Phipps Boone, in *The Petroleum Dictionary*, under Barrel, cites Wilson in support of the statement that the origin of the 42-gallon barrel was an agreement of West Virginia producers in 1886 (typographical error for 1866). Jerry Robertson, *Oil Slanguage*, defines barrel as follows: "42 U. S. gallons. Is the standard unit of measure for petroleum (crude oil) in all U. S. fields. Was first established legally in 1886 by the state of West Virginia." He must have been influenced in part by the information in *The Petroleum Dictionary*.

strike attracted a large number of oil seekers from all quarters. The Register[32] says the oil producers have issued the following circular: "Whereas, It is conceded by all producers of crude petroleum on Oil Creek that the present system of selling crude oil by the barrel, without regard to the size, is injurious to the oil trade, alike to the buyer and seller, as buyers with an ordinary size barrel cannot compete with those with large ones. We, therefore, mutually agree and bind ourselves that from this date we will sell no crude by the barrel or package, but by the gallon only. An allowance of two gallons will be made on the gauge of each and every 40 gallons in favor of the buyer."

Similar information regarding the agreement is given in *Derrick's Hand Book* (I, 704), where it is said that the agreement was made "by Dr. M. C. Egbert and the representatives of some thirty or more of the leading oil companies in the Oil Creek Valley. . . . This was virtually establishing 42 gallons as the standard measure for a barrel of crude oil." The agreement, including the names of those signing, appeared in the *Titusville Morning Herald* of August 20, 1866.

[32] Probably the *Weekly Register,* founded in 1862 by Walter R. Johns, who was also the editor. The paper was sold in 1866 to Henry A. Dow, "Who fathered the *Daily Register*"; McLaurin, *Sketches in Crude Oil,* 352. Giddens, *Birth of the Oil Industry,* 170, says that Johns, in January, 1862, established the *Oil City Register.* The *Register,* whatever may be its formal title, was published in Oil City, Pa.

The anonymous author of an article in *The Lamp* for October, 1932, and in the 75th Anniversary Edition (1957), and Charles Morrow Wilson, in his book, *Oil Across the World,* have interpreted the item quoted above from *Derrick's Hand Book* to mean that the agreement was made by West Virginia operators, but it appears that only the first sentence referred to West Virginia.[33] The item quoted says that the agreement was made by producers "on Oil Creek." That creek is in Pennsylvania. The resolution, in effect, says that in 1866 there was no standard container or barrel, which is in agreement with Smiley's account and other evidence here given.

It has been suggested, and the logic is sound, that a 40-gallon barrel as a unit of measure must have been fairly common in the period 1860–66, and that two gallons or 5 per cent was to be added by those signing the 1866 agreement in order to cover leakage or the presence of water and other impurities.[34] The addition of two gallons to make up for leakage and foreign substances is somewhat similar to a long-continued practice in the oil industry respecting the purchase of crude oil in a

[33] Wilson, *Oil Across the World,* 118; Douglas Reeves, "West Virginia's Burning Springs," *Baroid News Bulletin,* Vol. VIII, No. 2 (March–April, 1956), 14.

[34] W. M. Dunham, in the chapter, "Origin of the 42-Gal. Barrel," in Dorsey Hager, *Oil-Field Practice,* says that "40-gal. became the trade-custom barrel for crude oil . . . from 1860 to 1866," and the producers added "2 gal. for tare or waste."

lease or field tank. Each tank was strapped or measured so that the quantity of the liquid in the tank could be calculated for any level. Tables were prepared showing the quantity at each level. Since water and other foreign substances were usually mixed with the oil, the purchaser who ran a tank of oil did not get pure oil; consequently, the purchase contract in common use contemplated calculations on less than 100 per cent tank tables, or about 98 per cent.

Certainly, the agreement of the producers in 1866 was a strong influence in the ultimate fixing of a 42-gallon barrel as the unit of measure for crude oil, but other factors may be cited also. For instance, E. L. Hoffman, of the Socony-Vacuum Oil Company, says that Drake and his contemporaries used whiskey barrels of 42-gallon capacity and such may have been the origin of the 42-gallon measure.[35]

It is not difficult to believe that many whiskey barrels found their way into the oil regions in the 1860's and that they were quite satisfactory as oil containers. Moreover, large numbers of empty ones must have been available if there were many drinkers like Benedict Hagan. Hagan was a German immigrant who, while a boy living in the slums of New York, whipped Big Fist Flynn and took over the leadership of a gang of Irish dead-end kids, after which he announced that thereafter he was Irish and had the name Ben Hogan. The name stuck. A bio-

[35] "The Measurement of Petroleum," a paper given in 1952 before the National Conference on Weights and Measures.

graphical sketch of that extraordinary man has recently been written by Joseph Millard, based in part on *The Life and Adventures of Ben Hogan, the Wickedest Man in the World,* written by George F. Trainer under the supervision of Hogan in 1878. The Millard book, *The Wickedest Man,* describes Hogan as "the gentleman from hell" and the strongest man in the world. Hogan was not an "oil-field tough," for, although he spent riotous years in the oil-producing areas, he disdained real work in favor of fighting and drinking whiskey in large quantities. The book gives a vivid account of the oil-boom towns of the 1860's, along with proof that many whiskey barrels were made available for oil.

Hogan (or Hagan) was not a fictitious character. Much evidence supports the following statements in the foreword to the Millard book: "He was pirate, blockade runner, spy, bounty jumper, pimp, bartender, confidence man, showman. . . . The strongest man in the world, the uncrowned heavyweight bare-knuckle boxing champion, candidate for Congress, and, finally, a fighting evangelist."

Hogan was really tough, and, during most of his life, he exhibited no moral sense whatever. Moreover, he had unusual ability, willingness, and opportunity to indulge to excess in many of his vices. As yet, I have found no character in a novel about the petroleum industry that compares to Hogan. I have, as far as I know, the most complete collection there is of such novels in English, ninety titles. The only known item missing is *Black Gold,* by Arthur Catherall, published in London in 1939—one of four novels about the petroleum industry with the title *Black Gold*, three in English and one in Russian by Count Alexey N. Tolstoy.[36] *Black Gold,* by Jewel Gibson, uses vivid colors in painting tough boom-town characters, as does Clyde B. Ragsdale's *The Big Fist,* although both books seem to go too far in portraying a typical boom town and its inhabitants. Yet it may be said that a novelist would hardly dare to create a character as incredible as Hogan actually was. If he and his kind rendered any service, it was in their wholesale emptying of badly needed whiskey barrels.

Regarding the size of the whiskey barrel in the 1860's, Leo Vernon of the Continental Distilling Corporation[37] expressed the belief in a letter to me that the common barrel of the time was one of 42-gallon capacity. In brief, he says that the government's statutory table for evaporative loss is based on 40 gallons net at the time of fill, and that it is customary to allow for expansion; consequently, the total capacity of a container intended to hold 40 gallons of whiskey would be 42 gallons. Inquiries to several other distillers produced no positive information about the capacity of the whiskey barrel in the 1860's. To others will be left the search for further in-

[36] The authors of the other two novels published in English are Jackson Cole and Jewel Gibson. Tolstoy's novel, *Chronoye Zoloto,* was later renamed *Émigranty* (*The Émigrés*). As far as is known, this book has not been translated into English.

[37] September 27, 1954.

formation on the size of whiskey barrels in the 1860's and the sizes of containers for whale oil and coal oil that must have been among the tight containers that were sought. The question of whether someone made such a good barrel of 42-gallon capacity that it became the standard, I also leave for other hands.

The 42-Gallon Oil Barrel as a Unit of Measure

IT WILL BE remembered that the "tierce," a wine measure long in use in Great Britain and the United States, had a 42-gallon capacity, as did the fish barrel and the old English barrel for spruce beer; therefore, it is logical to believe that strong "tight" casks of 42-gallon capacity that had been used in the British Isles and the United States reached the oil fields and were used as models when the manufacturing of barrels for oil was begun.[1] It will also be remembered that the federal statute of 1879[2] dealt with imports of wines and liquors in "pipes,"

[1] In a short article by Bernard Goulston, "How Did the Barrel Get That Way," *Imperial Oil Review* (April, 1955), information is given about the gallon and the oil barrel. The speculation is that the tight British containers for wine and fish (42 gallons) were first adopted in the United States for whale and coal oil, and then for liquid petroleum. Goulson prefers to believe that "the tierce, in which knights of old stored wine, is a blood brother to today's oil barrel."

[2] 19 United States Code (U.S.C.). Sect. 467.

"tierces," and other containers; consequently, the "tierce" must have been a tight 42-gallon container made to established specifications and suitable for shipping oil.

As might be expected, the need for oil barrels not only stimulated the manufacture of barrels, but also increased applications for patents relating to barrels and other containers for oil or products. E. L. Hoffman quotes from "The Report of the Commissioner of Patents for the Year 1863" as follows: "Fourteen patents have been issued for more oil-tight barrels, besides as many for tanks and cans." Edward B. Swanson has taken the trouble to check those patent applications and was amazed to find that no mention was made of capacity and no data were given from which capacity could be accurately calculated.

Reference has been briefly made to the Scottish "cran" provided for in 1815.[3] A report to President Andrew Jackson in 1832 regarding fisheries quotes from the findings by the commissioners of the herring industry appointed to fix the size of the "cran," as follows:

The Commissioners for the herring industry, in virtue of the authority vested in them by the aforesaid act, hereby give notice, that from and after the first day of June, 1816, the cran to be used for the purchase and sale of fresh herrings, taken in the British herring industry, shall be of the content or capacity of forty-two gallons English wine measure, reckoning from the outermost extremities of the

[3] 55 George III, c. 94, par. XIII.

staves—that it shall be of oak staves completely sea-
soned, one-half part of an inch in thickness throughout of made work, at the least—the staves not to
be under two inches nor to exceed four inches in
breadth, and no croze to be allowed; that is, the cran
shall be well fired, and completely round; that it
shall be quarter bound with eight good hoops of
wood and four hoops of iron—the iron hoops to be
each an inch in breadth, and of sufficient thickness;
that two hoops of wood and one of iron shall be
placed on each quarter of the cran, the iron hoops to
be placed between the wooden ones, and, when fully
criven, to leave a space of nine or ten inches dis-
tance between the uppermost hoops of each quarter
at the bulge; that the ends of the cran shall be
hooped exactly in the same manner as the quarters
—with two hoops of wood and one of iron on each
end, and these to be driven so far down as to leave
three-fourths part of an inch bare, for the purpose
of being perforated with small holes, to allow the
water and slime to drain off while filling; and that,
when finished, the uppermost hoops, both of the
ends and quarters, shall be firmly nailed down, to
prevent them from coming off.

As no cran can be approved, of which is of greater
or less content or capacity than forty-two gallons
English wine measure, and as it is desirable to prevent the inconvenience that will arise to the curers
from making the dimensions at the first two small,
the commissioners deem it expedient that the length

of the cran shall be thirty-one inches of made work, that the bung diameter, exclusive of the thickness of the staves, shall be twenty-one inches, and that the diameter of the ends, taken correctly, from inside to inside, at the very extremity thereof, shall be eighteen inches; the mean diameter will thus be twenty inches and one-fourth part of an inch, and the contents forty-two gallons and one half, but care will be taken at the adjustment of the measure, and before it is branded, to reduce it to the exact gauge of forty-two gallons, by paring a little from the ends of the staves.[4]

Here were details for making a 42-gallon container for herring, and it had to be tight to prevent spoilage and the leakage of liquid. The information prompted Mr. Swanson to write to T. J. Garin, curator of the Drake Well Memorial Park, asking whether, in the Drake Museum, there was an old oil barrel or data concerning dimensions. Information given in Mr. Garin's reply of November 21, 1953, was reported by Mr. Swanson substantially as here set forth. The staff of the Museum searched the files of the *Pithole Daily Record,* the *Titusville Herald,* and other source material, but were unable to find any advertisements or news stories that gave dimensions of the staves to be used in the making of barrels. Garin did say that, in 1951, in order to shoot several scenes for the *Evolution of the Oil Industry* (probably the Bureau of Mines motion picture), it was necessary

[4] 22 Cong., 2 sess., *House Doc. No. 99.*

to find some old oil barrels. There were obtained from the Crew-Levick Company some old wooden barrels that had been on the premises of the company for a long time. A. C. Brown, of the museum staff, measured one of the old barrels. The stave had an over-all length of 33 1/4 inches (31 1/2 inches between the barrel heads), and the diameter of the head was 19 1/2 inches. Mr. Brown, who had had considerable experience in filling the old oil barrel, pointed out that the barrel never measured exactly 42 gallons—some held more, some less—so that the weight was always indicated first, then the gallonage was stencilled. The measurements given by Mr. Brown are not adequate for the calculation of the cubic capacity of the barrel, but there is some similarity with the dimensions given for the cran.

It has been suggested that barrels of 45 gallons were in use (the federal tax, already discussed, was $1.00 a barrel on each barrel of not more than 45 gallons), but in transporting the oil, especially over rough roads, leakage averaged three gallons, so that the unit finally became 42 gallons.[5] It is easier to establish the leakage than the common use of 45-gallon containers.

[5] Franklin B. Coyne, *The Development of the Cooperage Industry in the United States,* 35, expresses the opinion that in New England strong fish barrels (tierces) were probably used for shipping oil, and that in Massachusetts the tierce was of 45- or 46-gallon capacity, but the casks leaked some 2 or 3 gallons when filled with oil; consequently, the barrel of 42 gallons became the unit of measure. It is observed that Adams, in his 1821 report, referred to a Massachusetts stat-

Alfred W. Smiley, the "old-timer" who has already been quoted, gives support to the conclusion that 45 gallons were considered to be a barrel, but he does not say that containers of such capacity were available. This paragraph appears in his book, *A Few Scraps* (*Oily and Otherwise*):

> It should be remembered that in the early days of the business all the crude oil was handled in barrels. Forty-five gallons was considered a barrel up to the time when tanks at wells and on cars were measured, and their capacity, or contents, computed in bulk. After that forty-two gallons was by common consent accepted as a barrel of crude oil. In the refined business, however, the dealing has always been by the gallon, regardless of the capacity of the package.[6]

The use of tank cars on railroads did not become common until at least 1866,[7] and there is abundant evidence to show that in the early days of the industry, even to 1866, the 40-gallon barrel as a unit of measure for crude oil was as frequently used, perhaps more frequently, than the 45-gallon barrel. Moreover, as already set forth, there is much proof and logic to establish that, in the early days, efforts were made to get tight containers, such as

ute giving the usual capacity of 42 gallons to the tierce, not 45 or 46.

[6] Page 60.

[7] Giddens, *The Birth of the Oil Industry*, 151.

the tierce, the herring barrel, and the whiskey barrel. Although there may be some doubt whether the whiskey barrel in the middle of the nineteenth century (1850–66) had a 42-gallon capacity, there is no doubt regarding the tierce and the herring barrel. Furthermore, it is logical to believe that the manufacturers of barrels for crude oil used as models those tight containers and that the 42-gallon barrel, both as a container and a unit of measure, was at least as common as the 45-gallon barrel.

The statement by Smiley that has been quoted seems clearly to say that the 45-gallon barrel was replaced by the 42-gallon barrel as a unit of measure after crude oil began to be transported in bulk by railroad tank cars. As subsequent discussion will show, railroad rates for transporting crude in bulk were usually calculated on a 45-gallon barrel, not a 42-gallon barrel, for some years after bulk transportation on railroads began.

Neither the facts as I have found them nor reasonable conclusions drawn from the facts support Smiley's statement that "forty-five gallons was considered a barrel up to the time when tanks at wells and on cars were measured . . . [and] after that forty-two gallons was by common consent accepted as a barrel of crude oil."

Although the 42-gallon barrel for crude oil tended to displace other units of measure, its use was not well-established as late as 1875. S. F. Peckham, in his extraordinarily interesting and comprehensive "Report Upon the Production, Technology, and Uses of Petroleum and Its Products," made October 6, 1882, gives many refer-

Col. Edwin L. Drake

James M. Williams

Which one is father of North America's oil industry?

The Drake Well. The man in the silk hat is Drake.

ences to both 40-gallon and 42-gallon barrels.[8] There is, however, considerable evidence of the increasing use of the 42-gallon barrel after 1866, but other measures or units still persisted.[9]

[8] The report appears as pages 1–319 of the 10th volume of the quarto series, comprising the final report on the Tenth Census, published by the Department of the Interior in 1884. See pages 106, 107, 151, 153, 154 (40 gallons), and 98, 109, 150, 187, and 273 (42 gallons). On page 98, Peckham says that a Pennsylvania law of May 22, 1878, required reports regarding storage to be calculated on a barrel of 42 gallons. No reference was made to the use of a 45-gallon barrel with respect to crude oil.

[9] *Derrick's Hand Book*, I, 95, item of October 20, 1867, tells of the construction of a large storage tank in New Jersey with a "capacity of 24,000 bbls. of 42 gallons each"; on page 200, an item of January 8, 1873, reports a notice by the Miller and Sandy Pipe Lines that "42 gallons will constitute a barrel in all calculations of oil transported"; on page 837, giving estimates of production figures in several states for the period 1875–97, the estimates of the United States Geological Survey are calculated in barrels of 42 gallons; on page 308, an item of January 20, 1879, refers to a proposed tax by Pennsylvania of one cent a gallon, or forty-two cents a barrel. However, on page 84, an item of January 20, 1867, reads: "A meeting of exporters in New York City decides that the capacity of oil barrels shall be not less than 40 nor more than 46 gallons"; "Hepburn Report Exhibits," on page 422, states that railroad rates on oil in 1872 were based on a 45-gallon barrel, citing page 25 of Montague, *The Rise and Progress of the Standard Oil Company;* on page 233, an item of September 14, 1874, says that railroad rates on oil were based on a 45-gallon barrel; on page 969, an item reports that, because of a tariff applicable to shipments of oil in barrels by rail, tank car rates would also be the same, based on 45 gallons to the

Several items deserve special mention as proof of the confusion that existed as late as 1871, when the barrel was used as a unit of measure for oil. In *Derrick's Hand Book* (I, 831), is a facsimile of part of the *Titusville Daily Courier* of April 11, 1871. The paper shows that the report of daily average production for March and the shipments by rail had been calculated on a barrel of 43 gallons, while the figures given by the Empire Pipe Line for shipments by river had been calculated on a 42-gallon barrel, with figures by others calculated on a 45-gallon barrel. The paper says that, in estimating shipments of "oil packages we consider them as containing 46 gallons each." Production in barrels "for Franklin and Tidioute oil" were said to be calculated on 42 gallons to the barrel but for other tracts on 43 gallons. *Special Report on the Petroleum of Pennsylvania* by Henry E. Wrigley contains information on the measurement and sale of refined oil.[10] Calculations show a 46.238-gallon barrel.

Real hard times came to the oilmen in 1872. Production had increased materially and prices had decreased. From the high of nearly $10.00 a barrel in 1864, the average price in 1869 was about $5.35 a barrel; in 1870 it was about $3.85; in 1871 about $4.34; and in 1872 about $3.40. The latter was called "poverty price."[11] *Derrick's Hand*

---

barrel. Obviously, some of the references are to a unit of measure, not to the capacity of the containers.

[10] The report was made December 31, 1874, to Professor J. P. Lesley, and was printed as a booklet of 117 pages.

[11] C. D. Lockwood, "Ups and Downs of the Oil Business,"

Book (I), reveals many methods that were adopted to improve the situation, including agreements of producers to shut in wells until better prices were obtained. This is part of the item of October 13, 1872:

> At a session of the Council of Producers, the following resolution was passed: "Whereas, False reports have been circulated in the eastern markets to the effect that the producers intend starting their wells again at once; Resolved, That the Council instruct its executive officers to telegraph to some of the leading exporters in New York City an emphatic denial of said reports, and also decided not to resume pumping until the full 30 days have expired; also that we will have $5 per bbl. of 42 gallons for our crude oil."

Apparently there was no fear of antitrust laws, if any were on the books. The federal act (Sherman Act) was not passed until 1890.

More and more wells combined with other factors to make the shutdown agreements ineffective to establish a $5.00-a-barrel level, or even a $2.00 level, for the average price dropped to about $1.83 in 1873, and to $0.83 in 1875. However, it is logical to believe that the Resolution of the "Council of Producers" had much to do with the general acceptance in the 1870's of the 42-gallon bar-

a chart published in 1935 by the *Fort Worth Press;* McLaurin, *Sketches in Crude Oil,* 25, where the average yearly prices differ for some years from those given by Lockwood.

rel as a unit of measure. In *Derrick's Hand Book* (I, 704) in the chapter headed "The Crude Oil Market," this statement appears:

> Down to 1872 there was a considerable variation in the size of the barrel, which ranged all the way from 40 to 50 gallons, according to the fancy of the cooper or the cupidity of the buyer. The standard barrel of 42 gallons was adopted in 1872; this was one of the most practicable results accomplished by the Producers' movement of that year.[12]

Appraisal of all of this information doubtless leads to the conclusion that no one knows the true origin of the 42-gallon oil barrel as a unit of measure that is now firmly established in the United States, with an equivalent in Canada. There, a barrel of 35 Imperial gallons is employed. The difference between a barrel of 42 U. S. gallons (231 cubic inches) and a barrel of 35 Imperial gallons is 2.59 cubic inches if the Imperial gallon is taken to be 277.274 cubic inches and 7.70 cubic inches if the Imperial gallon is taken to be 277.42 cubic inches. In Great Britain and a number of other countries, the metric ton rather than the barrel is used for crude oil, but, as will be discussed, conversion tables minimize the complications.

While several fairly logical explanations have been advanced for the 42-gallon barrel's being adopted in the United States as the unit of measure for crude oil, it is

[12] Page 704.

believed that the Producers' agreement of 1866, fortified by the Producers' agreement of 1872, is the best. Assuming that such is the case, there remains the mystery of why the basis of sales was 40 gallons, to which 2 gallons were to be added as lagniappe.

Between 1872 and 1882, the 42-gallon barrel as a unit of measure for crude oil became so firmly established that the United States Geological Survey, beginning in the latter year, used it in its reports. However, for some years after 1882, a few agencies of the federal government gave statistics for imports and exports and refineries in 50-gallon units, although eventually the 42-gallon unit became standard.[13]

Presumably, the desire for accuracy prompted the United States Geological Survey to add an explanatory note to the annual Mineral Resources volumes for a period of five years, beginning with 1893, as follows: "The barrel used in this report, unless otherwise specified, is of 42 Winchester gallons."

The reference to the Winchester gallon seems to have been made through a mistake concerning the meaning of the term. In England, various standard measures were kept at Winchester and were identified by use of that name, such as Winchester gallon and Winchester bushel. In the section hereof that deals with the gallon, it was

[13] Letter from R. M. Gooding, petroleum chemist, Petroleum and Natural Gas Branch, United States Bureau of Mines, Department of the Interior, to W. T. Gunn, American Petroleum Institute, dated May 12, 1953.

pointed out that the Winchester gallon of Henry VII, as prepared in conformity with the 1497 statute, measured 268.43 cubic inches; that the Winchester gallon of Elizabeth (1601) measured 268.97 cubic inches; that the Guild Hall gallon of 1688, erroneously thought to be legalized as a substitute for the Winchester gallon, contained 224 (224.2) cubic inches; and that the Winchester bushel of William III (1702) was a dry measure of 2150.42 cubic inches, thus making a gallon of 268.8 cubic inches, on the assumption that a gallon is one-eighth of a bushel.

The Queen Anne, or wine gallon, of 231 cubic inches, effective in 1707, supplanted, as a legal measure, the Winchester gallon and remained the standard gallon in Great Britain until 1824, when the Imperial gallon of 277.42 cubic inches was adopted. The Queen Anne, or wine gallon, by state statutes and by custom, was used throughout the United States from Colonial days, and became the legal standard under a Senate resolution of 1830 and the approval of the action of the Honorable Louis McLane, secretary of the treasury, in fixing the gallon at 231 cubic inches. The bushel was fixed at 2150.42 cubic inches, corresponding to the Winchester bushel of William III. The bushel was a dry measure.

The wine gallon, whether it be that of Henry VII or Elizabeth (about 269 cubic inches), was not commonly used in the United States as a liquid measure; consequently, the explanatory note in the Mineral Resources volumes is ambiguous, or at least confusing. It should be said, however, that in the United States the term "Winchester gallon" has sometimes been used to mean a gallon of 231 cubic inches. Such was the definition given in *Appleton's Cyclopedia* and accepted as accurate by the courts in a number of lawsuits.[14] The intention in the note in the Mineral Resources volumes must have been to refer to the Queen Anne gallon of 231 cubic inches, and thus to make certain that no one could conclude that the gallon meant the British Imperial gallon of 277.42 cubic inches.

Although a barrel of 42 gallons is used as a unit of measure for crude oil, and now usually for other products as well, there is lacking a 42-gallon container, and it is rare indeed for crude oil to be stored or transported in barrels or casks. Instead, tanks much larger than a barrel are used to hold production and for storage, while tank cars, pipe lines, and tankers are used for transportation. For oil products, containers of many sizes are common, with the metal barrel or drum virtually displacing wooden containers.[15]

[14] *Nichols* v. *Beard,* 15 Fed. 435 (C.C.D. Mass. 1883); *State of Louisiana* v. *Standard Oil Co. of La.,* 188 La. 978, 178 So. 601 (1937); 27 *Corpus Juris,* 939.

[15] Dorothy F. Garretson, "The Barrel That Isn't," *Our Sun,* Vol. XIX, No. 3 (Summer, 1954), 16; Giddens, "When the Oil Barrel Was King," *DuPont Magazine,* Vol. XLVI, No. 5 (October–November, 1952), 8; H. S. Bell, *American Petroleum Refining,* 360. Bell gives use of containers of these sizes: 5, 10, 20, 32, 40, 45, 52, 55, and 60 gallons. George W. Todd, in his article, "Metal Drums and Barrels," used as a lecture in 1952–53 in the Department of Industrial Engineer-

It is odd that a woman, Elizabeth Cochrane, who married Robert L. Seaman, may properly be called the mother of the steel oil barrel. Shortly after 1900, after the death of her husband, she worked out and patented several containers, and her company (American Steel Barrel Company or Iron Clad Manufacturing Company) is credited with being the first to engage in mass production of steel barrels, producing as many as 1,000 a day by 1912. Few remember Mrs. Seaman for her great success (or her later failure) as a business woman. Her fame comes from being the young newspaperwoman who, in 1889, went around the world in seventy-two days, six hours, and eleven minutes, thereby beating the record of Phileas Fogg, of Jules Verne's story, *Around the World in Eighty Days.* Miss Cochrane made that world-publicized trip under the name Nelly (sometimes spelled Nellie) Bly. Fortunately, the story of that trip and of Nelly Bly's successes and misfortunes in the business world as the manufacturer of steel drums has recently been told in the book, *The Story of Nellie Bly,* published in 1951 by the American Flange and Manufacturing Company, Inc., of New York. The illustrations add much to the story of an extraordinary woman.

Although a container or barrel of 42-gallon capacity may have been in common use in the United States for crude oil after 1870, it has long since been abandoned;

---

ing, Columbia University, gives the history of the making of steel barrels and drums and much information regarding their use.

however, the barrel (42 gallons of 231 cubic inches) remains as the unit of measure. Such a unit seems to be definite, and it may appear to be quite simple to apply it. For instance, if it is desired to deliver to a purchaser from a field tank two barrels of crude oil into the purchaser's tank truck, one could fill a gallon bucket (exactly 231 cubic inches) eighty-four times and pour the oil into the tank truck; or, if the purchaser has a container of 19,404 cubic inches (84x231 cubic inches or two barrels), then it would be filled to the brim. If a larger quantity, say 1,000 barrels, is to be delivered to a pipe-line company through a line connected to the field tank, then one would continue to run oil from the tank until a level is reached so that, from the tank tables, a delivery of 1,000 barrels is shown. Unfortunately, accurate measurement is not that simple. More is required, even if the difference in levels indicates that 1,000 barrels have been removed.

While tank tables may be accurate, gauges often are not. Errors occur in reading and in listing levels, in making calculations, and in filling out "run tickets" (a statement of the number of barrels taken from the seller's tank). An article in *The Humble Way* declares that elimination of clerical errors in gauging is still difficult, but it is not as serious a problem as it was in the 1880's.[16] Reference is then made to an 1887 gauger's manual issued in Harmony, Pennsylvania, from which another company's policy is quoted:

[16] In the issue of May–June, 1956, page 21.

If the number of your errors in one month does not exceed four (4) per cent of the number of runs in that month, your wages for that month will be ninety ($90) dollars; if the number exceeds four (4) per cent, your wages for that month will be seventy-five ($75) dollars; if it exceeds ten (10) per cent, you will be liable to dismissal.

As will be explained, the barrel as a unit of measure for crude oil, if defined only as 42 gallons of 231 cubic inches, is not precise, even if it be assumed that no water or foreign substance is mixed with the oil. This is so because temperature and density (or specific gravity) affect the volume, and substantial changes in temperature will cause crude oil to expand or contract, changing the level of the oil in the container and, thereby, the number of cubic inches occupied by the liquid. Williams and Meyers, in their *Manual of Oil and Gas Terms,* give this definition of barrel: "42 U. S. gallons of oil at 60 degrees Fahrenheit." Even so, specific gravity should be taken into account.

That is why, for accuracy, it became necessary for the industry to adopt a standard temperature, which was 60° Fahrenheit, and to determine variations for oils of different specific gravities. Gravity is usually determined by a hydrometer like the one used in testing the liquid in the radiator of an automobile. The gravity scale that was adopted by the American Petroleum Institute (API) for crude oil has been the standard for many years, dis-

94

placing the baumé scale. Using a modulus of 141.5 and temperature of 60° Fahrenheit, the formulas for calculating the relation of API gravity and specific gravity are:

$$\text{Specific gravity} = \frac{141.5}{131.5 + \text{API gravity}}$$

$$\text{API gravity} = \frac{141.5}{\text{specific gravity}} - 131.5$$

Clearly, considerable mathematics would be involved in connection with the assumed delivery of 1,000 barrels of oil if calculations had to be made to correct for a temperature of the oil higher or lower than 60° Fahrenheit, considering its gravity. Fortunately, the National Bureau of Standards published the results of its original research in a paper called "Density and Thermal Expansion of American Petroleum Oils," designated as *Technologic Paper No. 77.* Supplemental information was also released as a circular or a supplement.[17]

The information from such research has been used to prepare what is usually called the Gravity Temperature Correction Table. With this table, the measured volume of crude oil of a known gravity and temperature can easily be increased or reduced to the figure that would be its volume at 60° Fahrenheit.[18]

[17] N.B.S. Circular C410 superseded Circular C154, with its supplements; supplements to Circular C410 have also been issued.

[18] A gravity-temperature correction table, as well as other tables and charts used in the petroleum industry, is included

Various methods have been used to avoid errors in gauging and subsequent clerical errors. The story is told in a recent issue of *The Humble Way*.[19] The method now used by the Humble Oil and Refining Company minimizes the onerous bookkeeping and calculating duties of gaugers in the field, because most of the work is done in the main office by machines. In a test, the company, under its old method, found 160 calculation errors in field reports for the Southwest Texas Division for January, 1955, while, under the new method, there were no errors for March, 1956.

To avoid errors, several companies have experimented with systems for automatic delivery of specified quantities of barrels of oil from the sellers' tanks. One such system has been developed by the Gulf Oil Corporation.[20] Such things as floats, timers, weirs, metering de-

---

in a well-known booklet, *Fisher-Tag Manual for Inspectors of Petroleum*. There have been at least twenty-seven editions. The twenty-seventh was copyrighted in 1946. Similar information is given in ASTM–IP *Petroleum Measurement Tables*. Interesting history and valuable information concerning measurement of oil are given by E. L. Hoffman in his paper, "The Measurement of Petroleum," which was delivered at the 37th National Conference on Weights and Measures held in Washington, D. C., in 1952.

[19] "Run Tickets on Tape," Vol. XII, No. 1 (May–June, 1956), 21.

[20] S. H. Pope and R. M. Stuntz, "Lease Automatic Custody Transfer Becomes a Reality," *Oil and Gas Journal*, Vol. LIV, No. 51 (April 23, 1956), 96. See R. L. Geer and D. C. Meyers, "Automatic Lease Production System," *The Petroleum Engi-*

vices, pumps, valves, temperature recorders, and the like operate automatically, while another device automatically takes samples for determination of API gravity and BS&W (basic sediment and water). Such a system is sometimes called Lease Automatic Custody Transfer. As long as everything works properly, the number of barrels to be delivered can be controlled with extraordinary accuracy, and the element of human error is largely avoided. All the same, the standards are many that must be met before the term "barrel of crude oil" becomes a definite unit of measure.

The time element must also be considered with respect to determination of quantity. A barrel of crude oil measured in a tank today may not be a barrel tomorrow, because of the shrinkage that occurs. Moreover, a specified number of barrels of crude oil in the original underground reservoir measure more than that number in the stock tank shortly after production. This is so because the change from reservoir pressure to the lower atmospheric

neer, Vol. XXVIII, No. 5 (May, 1956), B–49; M. H. Atkinson and A. H. Newberg, "Development and Application of Automatic Devices for Crude Oil Measurement," a paper presented to the 7th Annual Pipeline Conference (A.P.I.) in Houston on May 14, 1956; *Oil and Gas Journal,* Vol. LIV, No. 65 (July 30, 1956), 122. At the 1956 annual meeting of the Division of Production, American Petroleum Institute, three papers were given on the topic of automatic custody transfer of crude oil: H. C. Packard, "General Considerations"; Harold S. Kelly, "From the Producer's Viewpoint"; and A. H. Newberg, "From the Pipeliner's Viewpoint." These papers appear in *API Production Bull. No. 242,* Vol. 36 (1956), 15–33.

pressure results in considerable shrinkage, in part by escape from the liquid of gas and some of the lighter fractions. For instance, in the East Texas field, if round figures are used, 345,000 barrels of oil in the reservoir become about 272,000 barrels of oil in the stock tank. Contracts for purchase of a specified number of barrels of crude oil in the reservoir should state clearly whether the unit is a barrel as measured in the reservoir or in the stock tanks, with all the applicable corrections, as for gravity, temperature, and BS&W.

There are additional complications arising from terms used to designate quantity of crude oil. In a number of countries, quantities of crude oil are stated in metric tons, or some other unit of weight, thus necessitating considerable figuring to convert to barrels unless a conversion table is used. A ton is a unit of weight, while an oil barrel is a unit of liquid capacity, with corrections necessary for variations in temperature and gravity. A metric ton is 2204.622 pounds avoirdupois. Roughly, a metric ton of oil is about 7 1/2 barrels of 42 gallons of 231 cubic inches. Of course, the exact number of what might be called standard barrels in a metric ton depends on the gravity and temperature of the oil.

It may now not only be said that no one knows the origin of the 42-gallon oil barrel as a unit of measure, or knows why it was adopted in the United States, but it may also again be said that the unit as usually expressed (42 gallons of 231 cubic inches or 42 U. S. gallons) is far from being definite. That is why the companies that purchase large quantities of crude oil in the field from the producers include in each purchase contract, usually called "division order," provisions for accurately calculating the quantity, taking into account water, basic sediment, gravity, and temperature.[21]

This account of the barrel ends with another illustration of confusion and litigation that may occur by not defining accurately in a contract what is meant by "barrel." Unquestionably, by custom and usage in the United States, a barrel of oil, when used as a unit of measure, means 42 U. S. gallons or gallons of 231 cubic inches. However, in a number of states the weights-and-measures statute defines the barrel in different terms, as in Texas, where a barrel for liquids means 31 1/2 gallons. The Texas statute goes further by providing that all contracts relating to weights and measures made after the passage of the statute shall be construed according to the units fixed by the statute, unless there is an agreement to the contrary.[22] Therefore, in a state where such a statute is on the books, persons who draft contracts concerning crude oil or its products should take the pre-

[21] Some of the provisions of a typical division order are given in the opinion of the court in *State of Louisiana* v. *Standard Oil Co. of La.*, 188 La. 978, 178 So. 601 (1937). For various types of division orders, see Summers, *Law of Oil and Gas* (Perm.ed.), VII, c. 60.

[22] For an example, see Texas Laws 1919, Chapter 130, codified as Articles 5732 and 5736 of the Revised Civil Statutes of Texas, 1925. The amendment of Article 5732 in 1945 did not change the definition of any unit. Texas Laws 1945, c. 96.

caution of specifying a barrel of 42 U. S. gallons, if that is what is desired, for otherwise the definition of a "barrel" will be interpreted according to the laws of the state. Conversely, if, in such a state, the contract relates to a liquid other than oil, it should not be assumed that "barrel" will necessarily mean 42 U. S. gallons just because that is the accepted usage with respect to oil.[23] Finally, if oil is involved, the contractor who seeks accuracy rather than ambiguity should also provide for determination of quantity by appropriate corrections for gravity,

[23] In a Texas case, *Pope* v. *Joschke,* 228 S.W. 986 (Tex. Civ. App. 1921, writ dismissed), a contract was involved (date not shown), providing for the drilling of a water well that would yield sufficient water to fill 30 barrels each day. The contractor claimed that the word "barrel" meant 50 gallons. The owner of the property claimed that it meant 31 1/2 gallons. The appellate court held that there was testimony to justify a finding by the jury in the trial court that "barrel" meant 31 1/2 gallons. Although the appellate court referred to the Texas act of 1919 defining the barrel for liquids as 31 1/2 gallons, it is inferred that the act was passed after the contract had been executed, and that the act was referred to merely as indicating that, in common usage as found by the jury, a barrel meant 31 1/2 gallons and not 50 gallons. The opinion points out that the barrel, a liquid measure, is generally 31 1/2 gallons in the United States, one exception being the barrel for oil, which is 42 gallons. The opinion on the 42-gallon barrel related to common usage, and should not be interpreted as holding that, in Texas, a contract with respect to oil using the word "barrel" without definition will mean a barrel of 42 gallons instead of 31 1/2 gallons.

temperature, and BS&W, as well as for the time the determination is to be made.

It should not be supposed that the failure to include in a weights-and-measures statute a provision, as in the Texas statute, that the use of terms in a contract shall be given the statutory meaning unless otherwise defined, makes inapplicable the definitions in the statute. At least in regard to a contract made after the effective date of the statute, logic and court decisions support the view that the definitions in the statute would control unless the contract defined the terms otherwise or clearly showed the intended meaning.[24] However, this is not to say that a contract could not be reformed if the application of the statutory definition gave a meaning to the contract that did not express the agreement of the parties.

From all that has been set down in this record, it becomes clear that there is, even today, no clear-cut way of determining offhand just what a "barrel" of oil contains. It has been a fascinating ramble through a maze of statutes, court decisions, and customs. And at the end there remains the inevitable conclusion: The barrel can mean many different measures, depending upon many different factors, and even an ordinary, prosaic barrel of oil has behind it years of history, litigation, and even a smattering of romance.

[24] *State* v. *Moore*, 33 N.C. 70 (1850); *Clark* v. *Pinney*, 7 Cow. 681 (1827); 55 Am.Jur., Usage and Custom, Sec. 39.

Bibliography

1. Letters

Gooding, R. M. (petroleum chemist, U. S. Bureau of Mines). Letter to W. T. Gunn (API, New York), May 12, 1953.

Swanson, Edward B. (economist, retired, U. S. Department of the Interior). Letters to author, October 20, 1954, and November 4, 1955.

Vernon, Leo (chief counsel, Continental Distilling Corporation). Letter to author, September 27, 1954.

2. Government Publications

(a) Congressional

Adams, John Quincy. "Report Upon Weights and Measures," 16 Cong., 2 sess., *House Doc. Nos. 109–10, Senate Doc. No. 119.*

22 Cong., 2 sess., *House Doc. No. 99,* a report to President Andrew Jackson containing a report by commissioners of the herring industry.

Jefferson, Thomas. "Report on Weights and Measures,"
    1 Cong., 2 sess., *Doc. No. 15*.

39 Cong., 1 sess., *Joint Resolution No. 35*.

Report of Industrial Commission. 46 Cong., 1 sess., *House
    Doc. No. 476*. Washington, Government Printing
    Office, 1900.

(b) Statutes—United States

Internal Revenue Code of 1954, Sect. 4521.

13 Stat. 484.

14 Stat. 339; 15 U.S.C., Sect. 204.

20 Stat. 342; 19 U.S.C., Sect. 467.

21 Stat. 521; 15 U.S.C., Sect. 201.

Texas Laws 1919, c. 130, codified as Articles 5732 and
    5736 of the Revised Civil Statutes of Texas, 1925.

19 U.S.C., Sect. 467.

(c) Statutes—British

22 Edw. IV, c. 11 (1482).

55 George III, c. 94, par. XIII (c. 1810).

Pickering's Statutes at Large. A compilation of many
    volumes, beginning with statutes passed as early as
    1266.

Statutes of the Realm. 9 volumes (one in two parts),
    printed by command of King George III, the first
    volume in 1810, the last in 1882; containing statutes
    from 1235 through 1713. Supplemented by two in-
    dex volumes.

(d) Miscellaneous

Fischer, Louis A. "Modern Weights and Measures," a report published several times by the U. S. Bureau of Standards, Washington, D. C.

Hassler, Ferdinand R. "Reports" on weights and measures to the Secretary of the Treasury in 1931 and 1932, Washington, D. C.

Hoffman, E. L. "The Measurement of Petroleum," *Misc. Publication No. 206*, U. S. Department of Commerce, National Bureau of Standards.

Jones, Sarah Ann. *Weights and Measures in Congress (1775–1838)*. Misc. Publication, U. S. Bureau of Standards, Department of Commerce. Washington, Government Printing Office, 1936 (1938).

Peckham, S. F. "Report Upon the Production, Technology, and Uses of Petroleum and Its Products." Vol. X of *Tenth Census*, Department of the Interior, 1884.

Schwarz, Kathryn M. (compiler). *Federal and State Weights and Measures Through 1949 Enactments*. Washington, Government Printing Office, 1951.

"Special Report No. 7: Report of the United States Revenue Commission on Petroleum as a Source of National Revenue," Treasury Department, 1866.

3. Books

Alexander, John Henry. *Universal Dictionary of Weights and Measures, Ancient and Modern, Reduced to*

Standards of the United States of America. New York, Van Nostrand, 1867.

American Jurisprudence. "Usage and Custom," Vol. LV, Sec. 39. Bancroft-Whitney Company, San Francisco, and The Lawyers Co-operative Publishing Company, New York, 1942.

Appleton's Annual Cyclopedia and Register of Important Events. New York, D. Appleton & Company, 1862–1903.

Asbury, Herbert. *The Golden Flood.* New York, Alfred A. Knopf, 1942.

Bacon, Raymond F., and William A. Hamor. *The American Petroleum Industry.* New York, McGraw-Hill Book Company, and London, Hill Publishing Co., 1916.

Bell, H. S. *American Petroleum Refining.* New York, D. Van Nostrand Company, 1924.

Berriman, A. E. *Historical Metrology.* London, J. M. Dent & Sons., and New York, E. P. Dutton & Co., 1953.

Besant, Sir Walter, and James Rice. *The Golden Butterfly.* London, Tinsley Brothers, 1876.

Boone, Lalia Phipps. *The Petroleum Dictionary.* Norman, University of Oklahoma Press, 1952.

Boswell-Stone, W. G. *Shakespeare's Holinshed.* London, Lawrence and Bullen, 1896.

Botsford, Harry. *The Valley of Oil.* New York, Hastings House, 1946.

Burnell, George R., and John G. Swindell. *Wells and*

Well-Sinking. London, Crosby Lockwood and Son, 1882.

Century Dictionary and Cyclopedia. New York, The Century Company, 1914.

Clark, F. W. *Weights, Measures, and Monies of All Nations.* New York, D. Appleton, 1900.

Catherall, Arthur. *Black Gold.* London, Pearsons, 1939.

Cole, Jackson. *Black Gold.* New York, The William Caston Company, 1936.

Corpus Juris. Vol. XXVII. New York, The American Law Book Co., 1922.

Coyne, Franklin E. *The Development of the Cooperage Industry in the United States.* Chicago, Lumber Buyers Publishing Co., 1940.

Crew, Benjamin. *A Practical Treatise on Petroleum.* Philadelphia, Henry Carey Baird & Co., and London, Sampson Low, Marston, Searle & Rivington, 1887.

DeGolyer, E. *The Antiquity of the Oil Industry.* Dallas, privately printed, 1946.

Derrick's Hand Book of Petroleum. Vol. I. Oil City, Pa., Derrick Publishing Company, 1898.

Dictionary of National Biography. London, Oxford University Press, 1949.

Eaton, S. J. M. *Petroleum: A History of the Oil Regions of Venango County, Pennsylvania.* Philadelphia, W. P. Skelly & Co., 1866.

Egleston, Thomas. *Tables of Weights and Measures.* New York, John Wiley & Sons, 1899.

Encyclopaedia Britannica. 1910, 1949, and 1957 editions.

Erni, Henry. *Coal, Oil and Petroleum.* Philadelphia, Henry Carey Baird, 1865.

Fisher-Tag Manual for Inspectors of Petroleum. 28th ed. Chicago, Fisher Scientific Co., 1954.

Flynn, John T. *God's Gold.* New York, Harcourt, Brace and Company, 1932.

Forbes, R. J. *Bitumen and Petroleum in Antiquity.* Leiden, Netherlands, E. J. Brill, 1936; also Vol. I of *Studies of Ancient Technology.* Leiden, E. J. Brill, 1955.

Gale, Thomas A. *The Wonder of the Nineteenth Century: Rock Oil in Pennsylvania and Elsewhere.* Erie, Sloan & Griffeth, 1860. Facsimiles were printed for the Ethyl Corporation in 1952.

Gibson, Jewel. *Black Gold.* New York, Random House, 1950.

Giddens, Paul H. *The Birth of the Oil Industry.* New York, The MacMillan Company, 1938.

———. *Pennsylvania Petroleum 1750–1872, A Documentary History.* Titusville, Pa., Pennsylvania Historical and Museum Commission, 1947.

Hager, Dorsey. *Oil-Field Practice.* New York and London, McGraw-Hill Book Company, 1921.

Hallock, William, and Herbert T. Wade. *Outlines of the Evolution of Weights and Measures and the Metric System.* New York and London, The MacMillan Company, 1906.

Henry, J. T. *The Early and Later History of Petroleum.* Philadelphia, J. B. Rodgers Company, 1873.

Hepburn Report Exhibits, a part of *Report of the Special Committee on Railroads, Appointed . . . February 28, 1879, to Investigate Alleged Abuses in the Management of Railroads Chartered by the State of New York.* 8 vols. Albany, 1880, and New York, Evening Post Steam Presses, 1879, 1880.

Irving, Washington. *The Adventures of Captain Bonneville, U.S.A., in the Rocky Mountains and the Far West.* New York, G. P. Putnam and Sons, 1869.

Lincoln Library of Essential Knowledge. Buffalo, Frontier Press Company, 1944.

McLaurin, John J. *Sketches in Crude Oil.* 3rd. ed. Harrisburg, privately printed, 1902.

Measurement of Oil in Bulk. London, Institution of Petroleum Technologists, 1932.

Meyers, Charles J., and Howard R. Williams. *Oil and Gas Terms.* Albany, Banks and Company, and New York, Matthew Bender & Company, 1957.

Millard, Joseph. *The Wickedest Man.* New York, Fawcett Publications, Inc., 1954.

Montague, Gilbert Holland. *The Rise and Progress of the Standard Oil Company.* New York and London, Harper and Brothers, 1904.

Morris, Edmund. *Derrick and Drill.* New York, James Miller, 1865.

Nicholson, Edward. *Men and Measures.* London, Smith, Elder & Company, 1912.

Bibliography

Oldberg, Oscar A. *A Manual of Weights, Measures, and Specific Gravity.* Chicago, privately printed, 1885.

Parish, R. L., and John Myers. *The Story of Nelly Bly.* New York, The American Flange and Manufacturing Co., 1951.

Petroleum Measurement Tables. Philadelphia, American Society for Testing Materials, 1952.

Ragsdale, Clyde. *The Big Fist.* New York, G. P. Putnam's Sons, 1946.

Robertson, Jerry. *Oil Slanguage.* Evansville, Petroleum Publishers, 1954.

Seward, William H. *Life and Public Services of John Quincy Adams.* Auburn, N. Y., Derby Miller and Company, 1849.

Smiley, Alfred W. *A Few Scraps (Oily and Otherwise).* Oil City, Pa., Derrick Publishing Company, 1907.

Summers, Walter L. *The Law of Oil and Gas.* Vol. VII. Kansas City, Vernon Law Book Company, 1939.

Tolstoy, Count Alexey N. *Chornoye Zoloto (Black Gold).* Berlin, 1931, and Moscow, 1932. (No English translation.)

Wilson, Charles Morrow. *Oil Across the World.* New York, Toronto, and London, Longmans, Green and Company, 1946.

World Weights and Measures. Handbook for Statisticians. New York, United Nations, 1955.

Wrigley, H. E. *Special Report on the Petroleum of Pennsylvania.* Titusville, Pennsylvania Geological Department, 1874–75.

4. Periodicals

Bignell, L. G. E. "What is the Origin of the 42-Gallon Oil Barrel?" *Oil and Gas Journal,* Vol. XXXV, No. 39 (February 11, 1937), 69.

Botsford, Harry. "The Pipe Line War—Brief and Decisive," Cities Service *Service* (July, 1956), 19.

Burns, William H. "The Country's First Oil Company," *Our Sun,* Vol. XXI, No. 4 (Autumn, 1956), 37.

Cronin, Fergus. "North America's Father of Oil," *Imperial Oil Review,* Vol. XXXIX, No. 2 (April, 1955), 16.

Garretson, Dorothy F. "The Barrel That Isn't," *Our Sun,* Vol. XIX, No. 3 (Summer, 1954), 16.

Geer, R. L., and Meyers, D. C. "Automatic Lease Production System," *The Petroleum Engineer,* Vol. XXVIII, No. 5 (May, 1956), B–49.

Giddens, Paul H. "When the Oil Barrel Was King," *DuPont Magazine,* Vol. XLVI, No. 5 (October–November, 1952), 8.

Goulston, Bernard. "How Did the Barrel Get That Way?" *Imperial Oil Review,* Vol. XXXIX, No. 2 (April, 1955), 14.

"Just Who Did Start This Oil Business Anyway?" *Our Sun,* Vol. XXI, No. 1 (Winter, 1956).

Kelly, Harold S. "Automatic Custody Transfer of Crude Oil: From the Producer's Viewpoint." *API Production Bull. No. 242,* Vol. 36 (IV) (1956), 21.

The Lamp, Vol. XV, No. 3 (October, 1932), 8.

Menzing, LeRoy. An account of Canadian and United States claims to being "father of the oil industry" in North America, *Fort Worth Star-Telegram,* October 23, 1955, Section 3, Page 1.

Newberg, A. H. "Automatic Custody Transfer of Crude Oil: From the Pipeliner's Viewpoint," *API Production Bull. No. 242,* Vol. 36 (IV) (1956), 29.

Oil and Gas Journal, Vol. XIX, No. 46 (April 15, 1921), 62.

Oil and Gas Journal, Vol. XXXII, No. 26 (November 16, 1933), 65.

Oil and Gas Journal, Vol. LIV, No. 65 (July 30, 1956), 122.

"Oil on the Move," *Baroid News Bulletin,* Vol. VII, No. 2 (March–April, 1955), 27.

Packard, H. D. "Automatic Custody Transfer of Crude Oil: General Considerations," *API Production Bull. No. 242,* Vol. 36 (IV) (1956), 15.

"Petroleum's First Book," *Ethyl News* (September–October, 1957).

Pope, S. H., and R. M. Stuntz. "Lease Automatic Custody Transfer Becomes a Reality," *Oil and Gas Journal,* Vol. LIV, No. 51 (April 23, 1956), 96.

Reeves, Douglas. "West Virginia's Burning Springs," *Baroid News Bulletin,* Vol. VIII, No. 2 (March–April, 1956), 14.

"Run Tickets on Tape," *The Humble Way,* Vol. XXII, No. 1 (May–June, 1956).

Silliman, Benjamin. "Notice of a Fountain of Petroleum,

Called the Oil Spring," *The American Journal of Science and Arts*, Vol. XXIII, No. 1 (January, 1833), 97.

Skinner, F. G. "The Imperial Gallon and Its Forerunners from Saxon to Modern Times," *The Monthly Review* (May, 1953), 116.

5. Miscellaneous Sources

Atkinson, M. H., and A. H. Newberg. "Development and Application of Automatic Devices for Crude Oil Measurement," a paper presented to the Seventh Annual Pipeline Conference (API) in Houston, May 14, 1956.

Lockwood, C. D. "Ups and Downs in the Oil Business," a chart printed and distributed by the *Fort Worth Press* in 1935, giving much information for the period from 1857 to 1934 on oil prices, wells drilled, production, imports, important events, taxes, and the like.

Todd, George W. "Metal Drums and Barrels," a lecture given in the Department of Industrial Engineering, Columbia University, 1952–53.

6. Cases

Allen v. *Palmer*, 136 Pa. St. 556, 26 Atl. 516 (1890).
Borys v. *Canadian Pacific Ry. Co. et al.*, 4 W.W.R. (N.S.) 481, 1 Oil & Gas Reporter 605 (Alberta Supreme

Court 1952), affirmed by Privy Council, 1 All E.R. 451, 2 Oil & Gas Reporter 1597 (1953).

Ceballos v. *United States,* 146 Fed. 380 (C.C.A. 2d Cir. 1906, affirming 139 Fed. 705).

Clark v. *Pinney,* 7 Cow. 681 (1827).

Kitchen v. *Smith,* 101 Pa. St. (5 Outerbridge) 452, 457–58 (1882).

Kier v. *Peterson,* 41 Pa. St. (5 Wright) 357 (1862).

Nichols v. *Beard,* 15 Fed. 435 (C.C.D. Mass. 1883).

Pope v. *Joschke,* 228 S.W. 986 (Tex. Civ. App. 1921, writ dismissed).

Riggs v. *Armstrong,* 23 W. Va. 760 (1885).

State of Louisiana v. *Standard Oil Co. of La.,* 188 La. 978, 178 So. 601 (1937).

State v. *Moore,* 33 N.C. 70 (1850).

Stradley v. *Magnolia Pet. Co.,* 155 S.W. 2d 649 (Tex. Civ. App. 1941, writ refused).

Stroud v. *Guffey,* 3 S.W. 2d 592 (Tex. Civ. App.), 16 S.W. 2d 527 (1929, Comm. of App.).

Truby v. *Palmer,* 3 Pa. St. 156, 6 Atl. 74 (1886).

Wood County Pet. Co. v. *West Virginia Co.,* 28 W. Va. 210, 57 Am. Rep. 659 (1886).

Index

Adams, John Quincy: 19, 21; report on weights, 41
Alexander, John Henry: 7, 42
Antitrust laws: 87
American Petroleum Institute: and measurement of oil, 94, 95
Assay taste (unit of measure): 34

Barker, Thomas: 14–15
Barley: used as standard of measure, 6
Barrel: 32, 34, 40, 41; "tight," 22; of flour and bread, 22; of salt, 22; of corn, 22; history of, 29–46; defined, 30–31; kinds in English metrology, 30–31; as container for various commodities, 30ff., 43; in 1577, 35; wine, 30, 41, 43; English standards for (Henry VIII's reign), 38–40; history of use of term in U. S., 45–46; in early oil industry, 59; 40–gallon, 61ff., 66, 74–75, 83–84; defined by U. S. states prior to 1821, 62; double meaning of, 64–65; lawsuit about capacity, 1868, 67–68; whiskey, 75, 77–78; capacity in 19th century, 84; manufacture of, stimulated by oil industry, 79; confusion regarding capacity, 86–87; capacity in Canada, 88–89; *see also* 42-gallon barrel *and* oil barrel
Barrel, 42-gallon: in common use, 1866, 67; account of origin of, 68ff., 72–73; as unit of measure, 78–101; details for making, 79–81; measurement of, 82; in 1870's, 87; container lacking, 91; manufacture of, 92–93; specified for oil, 94

THE OILMAN'S BARREL

was set in 11-point Caledonia leaded three points. Caledonia, first cut in 1940, is an original design by W. A. Dwiggins for the Linotype Corporation. While Caledonia has the feeling of the Scotch faces it was derived from, it is lighter and better suited to present taste than its antecedents.

UNIVERSITY OF OKLAHOMA PRESS

NORMAN